# PUZZLE FUN
# TRAVEL
## Activity
# BOOK

D0317692

This edition published in 2020 by Arcturus Publishing Limited
26/27 Bickels Yard, 151–153 Bermondsey Street,
London SE1 3HA

Copyright © Arcturus Holdings Limited

All rights reserved. No part of this publication may be reproduced,
stored in a retrieval system, or transmitted, in any form or by any means,
electronic, mechanical, photocopying, recording, or otherwise, without
prior written permission in accordance with the provisions of the
Copyright Act 1956 (as amended). Any person or persons who do any
unauthorized act in relation to this publication may be liable to criminal
prosecution and civil claims for damages.

Author: Lisa Regan
Illustrators: Beccy Blake (interiors) and Berta Maluenda (cover)
Designer: Everitt Editorial
Editor: Joe Harris

CH007951NT
Supplier 40, Date 0620 Print run 10176

Printed in the UK

# LOOKING LOST

Help the penguin through the world maze
to reach its friends at the South Pole.

**What do you get if you put a wizard at the South Pole?**
A cold spell!

3

# HOLIDAY READING

What should an explorer read about before visiting the jungle?

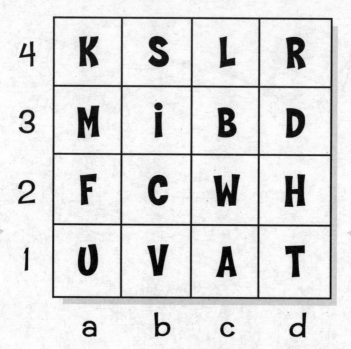

| | a | b | c | d |
|---|---|---|---|---|
| 4 | K | S | L | R |
| 3 | M | i | B | D |
| 2 | F | C | W | H |
| 1 | U | V | A | T |

c3.a1.b4.d2.

_____

b2.d4.c1.a2.d1

_____

**What did the boy say after reading for too long in the sun?**
"Hmm, I'm certainly well red!"

# DOODLE BUG

What kind of creature is this?
It can be as beautiful or as menacing as you like!

**What happened to the dog that swallowed a firefly?**
It barked with de-light!

5

# BIRD BRAINS

Solve the clues and write each number next to the correct picture. Once they're all in the right place, each horizontal, vertical, and diagonal row of three, should add up to 15.

1. It can fly and feeds on fish.
2. Has a distinctive forked tail.
3. It could be called a hammerhead!
4. This bird can't fly.
5. Often swims in the ocean.
6. Tiny bird that drinks from flowers.
7. Bright and noisy.
8. Graceful in the water.
9. A bird of prey.

**What do you call a man with a seagull on his head?**
Cliff!

6

# RAFT RACE

These explorers are all at sea! Try to find eight differences between the two pictures.

**Why are pirates called pirates?**
Because they arrrrrrrrrhh.

# BY THUNDER!

Work out which letters of the alphabet are missing, and then arrange them to form the name of the Roman god of the sky and lightning.

F O D G Q L Y K W M C V H X Z A N S B

- - - - - - -

**What do the Greek gods drink for breakfast?**
Orange Zeus!

# SNOW SHOES

Which explorer has walked farthest from the North Pole? Add up the numbers for each to find out.

What falls at the North Pole but never gets hurt?

ꜱnow

# HIDDEN TREASURE

What is hiding here? Shade any area black that contains a • to see what you find, and then finish the picture for yourself.

**What does Mowgli sing at Christmas?**
"Jungle Bells, Jungle Bells."

# FEARSOME FUNGUS

This mushroom has a truly awesome name!
Use the code to work out what it's called...

| D | E | F | G | H | I | J | K | L | M | N | O | P |
|---|---|---|---|---|---|---|---|---|---|---|---|---|
| A | B | C | D | E | F | G | H | I | J | K | L | M |

| Q | R | S | T | U | V | W | X | Y | Z | A | B | C |
|---|---|---|---|---|---|---|---|---|---|---|---|---|
| N | O | P | Q | R | S | T | U | V | W | X | Y | Z |

G H V W U R B L Q J
_ _ _ _ _ _ _ _ _ _

D Q J H O
_ _ _ _ _

**Why did the fungus leave the party?**
There wasn't mushroom!

11

# TINY TERRORS

Which one of these bugs does not match any of the others?

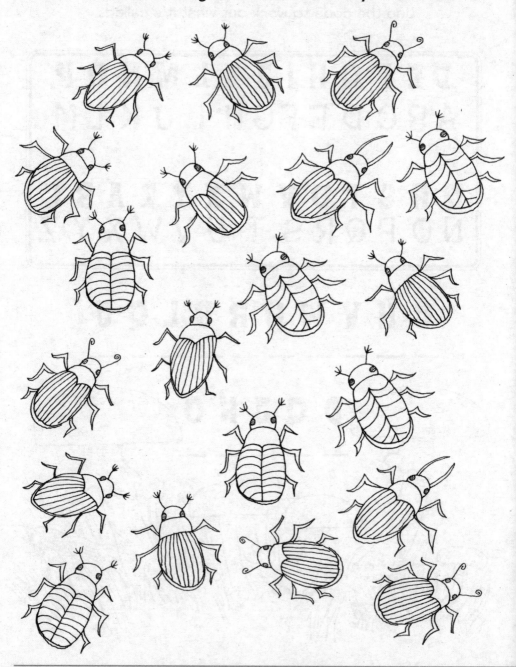

**What did the cat say to the flea?**
"Stop bugging me!"

# DUCK BILLS

Which two ducks' bills equal the same amount?

8 x 12

180 ÷ 2

108 - 14

85 + 13

3 x 32

4 x 26

285 ÷ 3

---

**What did the burglar's daughter play with at bathtime?**

A robber ducky!

# SUPER SUB

Copy the picture of the submarine using the
grid to help you.

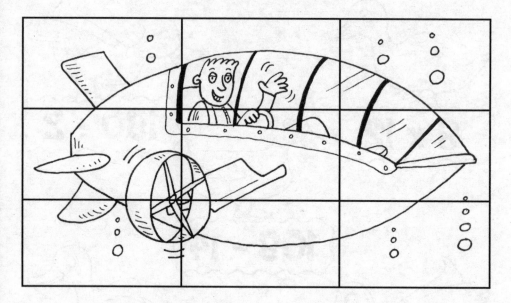

**What can fly underwater?**
A wasp in a submarine!

# BLIZZARD WARNING

How many snowflakes are falling here? Count them before they melt!

# MAP IT OUT

Fill in the map so there is one of each symbol in every row, column, and mini-grid.

# HOWL DO YOU DO?

How many new words of three or more letters can you make from the phrase below? One is there already to get you started.

# HUNGRY LIKE THE WOLF

1. GROWL
2. _____
3. _____
4. _____
5. _____
6. _____
7. _____
8. _____
9. _____
10. _____
11. _____
12. _____
13. _____
14. _____
15. _____
16. _____

**Why should you never trust the big bad wolf when he's in bed?**
Because he's lying!

# SEVEN SALMON SWIMMING

Find a way upriver, using only salmon that have numbers from the seven times table.

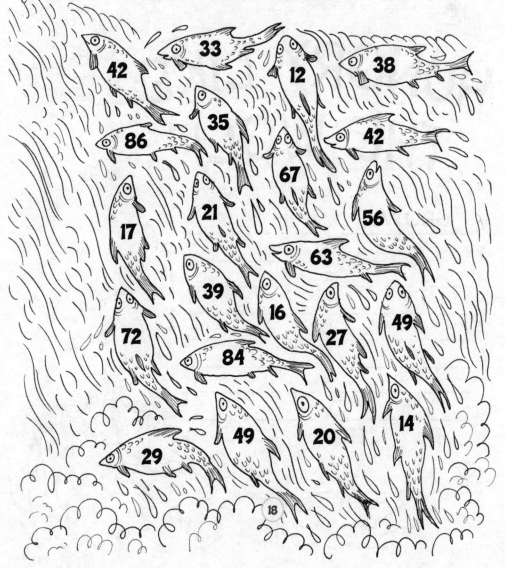

42 33 12 38 35 86 42 67 17 21 56 63 39 16 49 72 84 27 49 20 14 29

18

**Which fish come out at night?**
Starfish!

# LET US PRAY

Which of the spooky shapes is an exact match for the praying mantis?

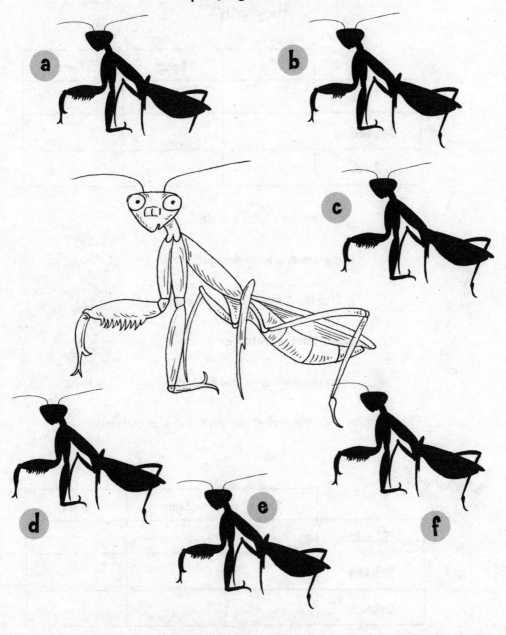

**What kind of insect hates Christmas?**
A bah humbug!

# BIRD LOVERS

Tim, Lucy, and Alex are at the zoo. They each see a different bird with a different relative. Who sees what, and who are they with?

|  | Tim | Lucy | Alex |
|---|---|---|---|
| Dad |  |  |  |
| Granddad |  |  |  |
| Aunt |  |  |  |

Tim isn't with his dad.

Lucy sees a long-legged bird.

The aunt sees the vulture.

Alex isn't with his granddad.

Tim doesn't see the vulture.

The person with their dad doesn't see the ostrich.

|  | Tim | Lucy | Alex |
|---|---|---|---|
| Stork |  |  |  |
| Vulture |  |  |  |
| Ostrich |  |  |  |

**What do you call two birds in love?**
Tweethearts!

# TREASURE MAP

Cross out any letter that appears more than once to find the name of a species of fish that is only found in the depths of the ocean.

# IT CAME FROM SPACE!

Draw whatever you think made this enormous crater. Was it a meteorite, an explosion, or just a really big hailstone?!

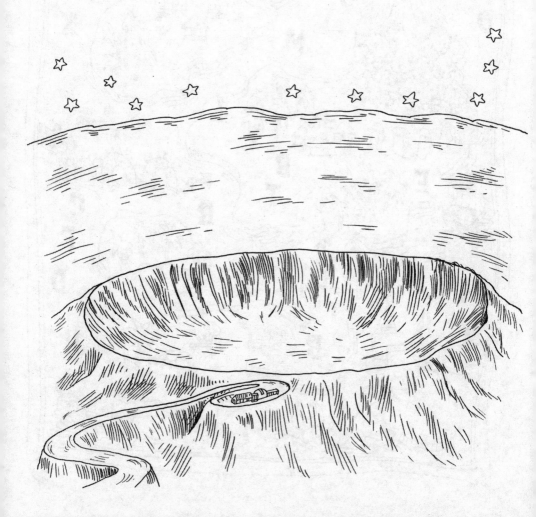

What did one volcano say to the other volcano?
"I lava you!"

# JUNGLE EXPLORERS

Get ready for an expedition into the jungle! How many times can you find the word JUNGLE hidden in the grid? Look forward, backward, and even diagonally.

```
G J E G U G J G U J
J L J L J E N U N U
U G L E G J G U N G
N G E L G N U J U J
L J E G U E U U G U
G U L N G U G J E N
U U J U E L G U J G
G G U J G J G L E L
J U G U J G J J G E
J J U N G L E J U G
```

Which river do snakes love the most?

The Hississippi!

23

# TIGER FEET

Find a way from the tiger's head to his tail.
Move up, down, or sideways, stepping only on the
paw prints like this one. 🐾

---

**What do you call a tiger at the beach?**
Sandy Claws!

# A RARE FIND

Find a way through the maze to reach the beautiful orchid in the middle.

**START**

**Why is the letter A like a flower?**

Because a B comes after it!

# ON THE WING

Work out which letters of the alphabet are missing, and then arrange them to find the name of this creature. Clue: the first part of its name means "moon"!

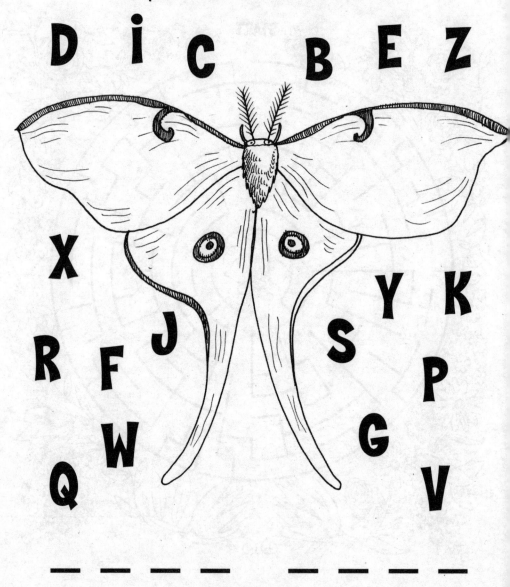

D I C C B E Z

X

Y K

R F S P

J G

W

Q V

\_ \_ \_ \_ \_ \_ \_ \_ \_ \_ \_

**Why shouldn't you be mean to a butterfly?**
Because you might hurt its feelers!

# HOME TO ROOST

What on earth could have built a nest like this?
Draw an enormous imaginary bird.

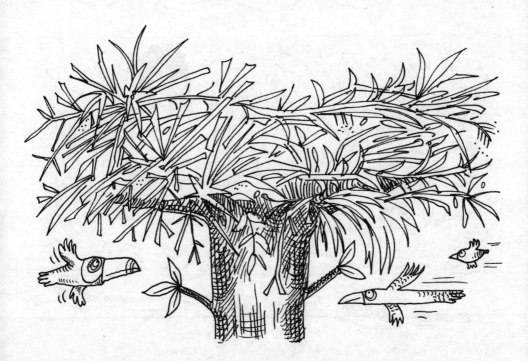

**What did the bird say as it finished building its nest?**
"That's the last straw!"

# FISHING FRENZY

If each piranha is worth 7 points, and each eel is worth 5 points, who has earned the most points with their catch?

**Why was Al Capone best friends with a fisherman?**
They got along by hook or by crook!

# TENT-ING FATE!

Study the two scenes and spot the eight differences between them.

**Why don't owls date in thunderstorms?**

It's too wet to woo!

# SOMETHING MISSING

Work out which letter is missing from this whole puzzle, then fill the holes to find six deserts.
Clue: it isn't even used in the instructions!

_T_C_M_

P_T_GONI_N

S_H_R_

_R_BI_N

K_L_H_RI

CHIHU_HU_N

# LAZY BONES

Which sloth has slept the longest?
Work out which has the biggest
number to get the answer.

$121 \div 11$

$\frac{1}{2}$ of 28

$144 \div 12$

$\frac{1}{3}$ of 36

**Why did cavemen love to eat sloths?**
They knew that fast food was bad for you!

31

# SNAKES ALIVE!

Which of the numbered sections actually appears in the large picture?

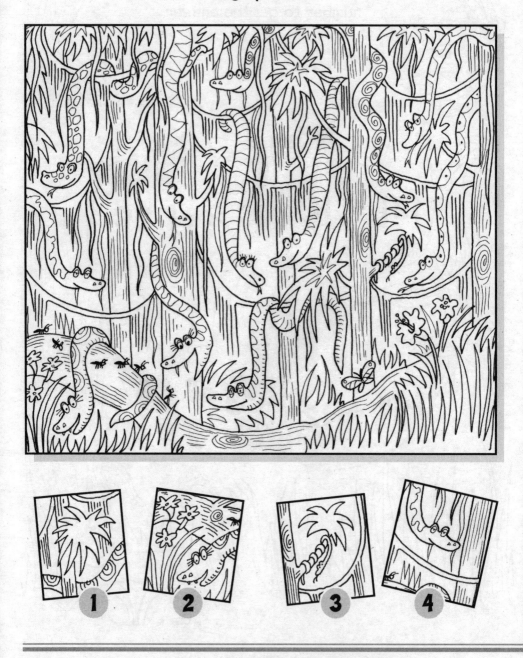

**Did you hear about the snakes that argued?**
They agreed to hiss and make up!

# READY, AIM, FIRE!

Use the code key to help you work out the name of this creature, which can spray chemicals from its rear end to keep away its enemies!

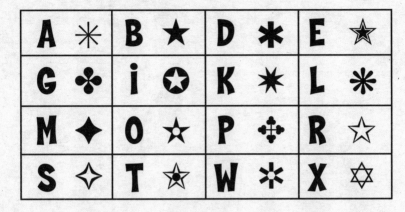

| A ✳ | B ★ | D ✳ | E ☆ |
| G ♣ | i ✪ | K ✳ | L ✳ |
| M ◆ | O ☆ | P ✤ | R ☆ |
| S ✩ | T ✯ | W ❋ | X ✡ |

★ ☆ ◆ ★ ✳ ☆ ✳ ✪ ★ ☆

_ _ _ _ _ _ _ _ _ _

★ ★ ★ ✯ ✳ ★

_ _ _ _ _ _

**Why are frogs always happy?**
Because they can eat whatever bugs them!

33

# BIRDS OF A FEATHER

Which one of these feathers does not match
any of the others?

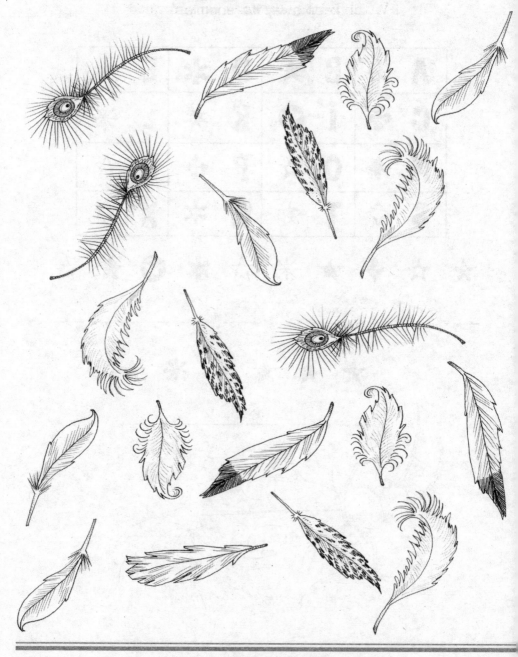

**Why did Archaeopteryx always catch the worm?**
It was an early bird!

# STAR PUPIL

Add together all the numbers on the chunky starfish,
and then subtract the numbers on the skinny brittle stars.
Which of the answers do you get?

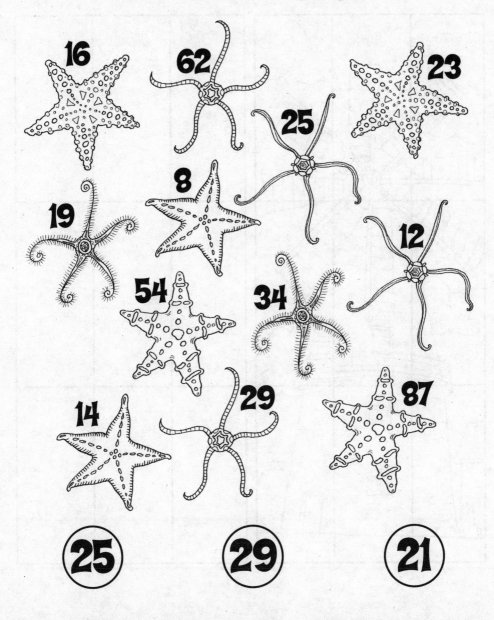

**Did you hear about the guppy that went to Hollywood?**
It became a starfish!

35

# CATCH THE WIND

Copy the picture of the windmill using
the grid to help you.

**How do lighthouse keepers communicate with each other?**
With shine language!

# COMPASS POINTS

How many compasses are there? And how many are not pointing North?

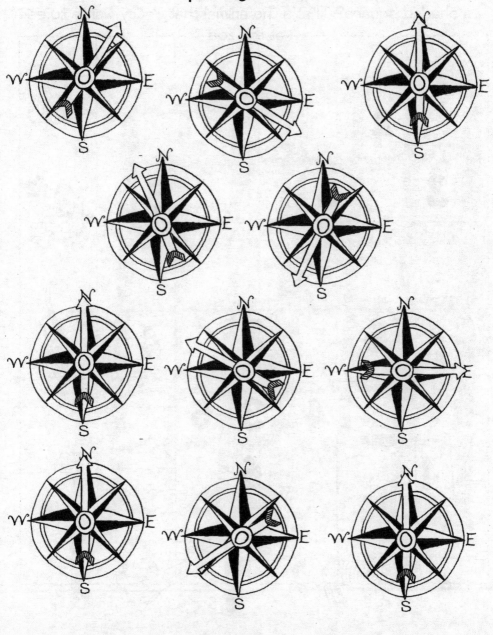

What do you call a creature that gets lost when there's a full moon?

A where-wolf!

37

# ZOO-DOKU

Fill in the blanks so that the numbers 1 to 6 appear in each row, column, and mini-grid. Which number doesn't appear in a shaded square? That's the animal that Beccy wants to see at the zoo.

**What has sharp teeth and lives at the end of the rainbow?**
The croc of gold!

# A WONDERFUL WORLD

How many new words of three or more letters can you make from the phrase below? One is there already to help get you started.

## CIRCLE OF LIFE

1. ICICLE
2. _____
3. _____
4. _____
5. _____
6. _____
7. _____
8. _____
9. _____
10. _____
11. _____
12. _____
13. _____
14. _____
15. _____
16. _____

**What do you call a girl with a flower on her head?**
Lily!

# ON THE ROCKS

Which of the creatures has Jon found in the rockpool?
Use the clues to work it out.

It has arms
or legs.

It doesn't have
pincers.

It isn't striped.

**What happened when they played cards on Noah's Ark?**
The game was ruined by two cheetahs!

# WEATHER FORECAST

The same wrong letter has been added several times on each line. Cross it out! You will be left with an old proverb.

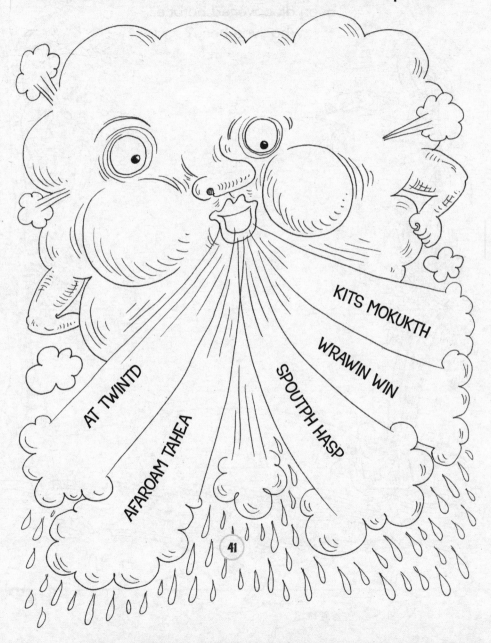

KITS MOKUKTH

WRAWIN WIN

SPOUTPH HASP

AT TWINTD

AFAROAM TAHEA

41

---

**Why shouldn't you argue with a weatherperson?**
They might storm out on you!

# DESERT ISLAND

While exploring, you come across an island that's never been discovered before. Who lives here?

**Where was the Declaration of Independence signed?**
At the bottom!

# BLACK AND WHITE

All of the creatures hidden in this grid have striking black and white patterns. See if you can find them all.

ORCA      PENGUIN      TAPIR

PANDA      LEMUR      COLOBUS

BADGER      OSPREY      ADDER

ZEBRA      SKUNK      MAGPIE

| R | W | i | T | Z | P | H | M | O | F |
|---|---|---|---|---|---|---|---|---|---|
| T | M | A | D | D | E | R | E | D | L |
| H | A | P | Y | i | N | B | O | A | E |
| T | G | C | E | O | G | W | R | R | M |
| E | P | O | R | T | U | R | E | A | U |
| G | i | Z | P | O | i | D | G | O | R |
| P | E | i | S | O | N | W | D | L | i |
| C | O | L | O | B | U | S | A | R | P |
| A | D | N | A | P | N | G | B | E | A |
| D | K | N | U | K | S | B | O | G | T |

---

Q: What do you get if you cross a Roman emperor with a boa constrictor?

Julius Squeezer!

# GOING NUTTY

Squirrel is gathering nuts for the winter. Guide him
to his nest, moving sideways or up and down,
following the treats in this order:

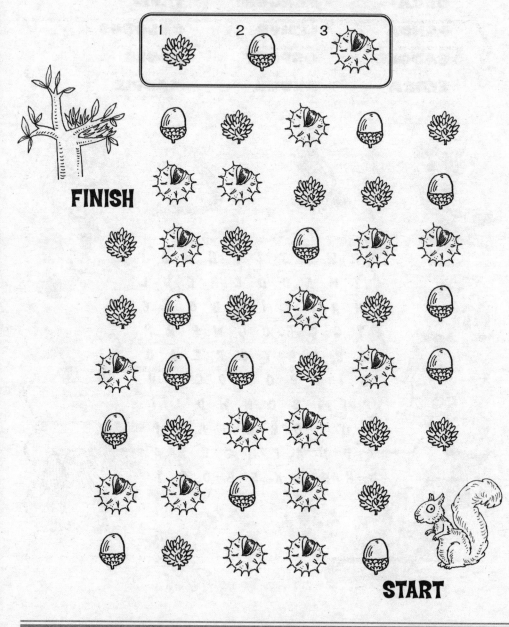

**FINISH**

**START**

**What's the difference between an oak tree and a tight shoe?**
One makes acorns, the other makes corns ache!

# BEETLE RUN

Find a way from the top to the bottom without stepping on any beetles along the way.

**What do you call a dead fly?**
A flew!

# HOO AM I?

Work out which letters of the alphabet are missing, and then rearrange them to find a species of owl.

Missing letters: _ _ _ _ _

Answer: _ _ _ _ _

Why did the owl 'owl?
Because the woodpecker would peck 'er!

# OCEAN GIANT

This submariner has come face to face with an undersea giant. What do you think it is?

**Little sister: Why is our goldfish orange?**

Big brother: Because the water makes it rusty!

# WINDY DAY

Study the wind speeds and directions to work out which is the odd one out.

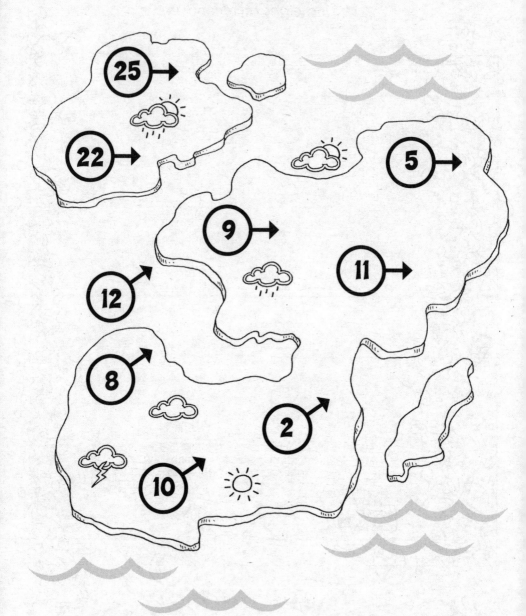

**What's the best day for sailing?**
Winds-day!

# MIGHTY MAYA

The Maya people lived in and around Mexico, hundreds of years ago. Study the picture of this amazing building and try to find eight differences.

**When did Montezuma die?**
A few days before they buried him!

# WILD THINGS

Each of the groups of letters is an anagram of a wild animal. Try to work out what they are. Watch out—they bite!

HEANY

LIARLOGTA

BOABON

RUGAJA

LIARLOG

TOCYOE

**Why should you never sleep with your head under the pillow?**
Because the tooth fairy might take all your teeth!

# MEGA BLAST

Add the symbols +, −, x, and ÷ in the correct order to make the volcano blast equal exactly 100.

= 100 !

60 ? 20 ? 50 ? 3 ? 2

What kind of trees do mathematicians like?
Geometrees and trigonometrees!

51

# PERFECT PATTERN

Use pastel shades to fill each section marked with ● to reveal a wonder of nature. Then finish the background however you like.

52

**What did the leaf say when it fell from the tree?**
Nothing, leaves don't talk!

# NO PLACE LIKE HOME

Use the code to work out the names of these four birds, which are all unusual because they don't build a nest.

Code:

A = B, B = C, C = D, and so on. (Z = A)

JHMF

_ _ _ _

ODMFTHM

_ _ _ _ _ _ _

QZYNQAHKK

_ _ _ _ _ _ _ _ _

BTBJNN

_ _ _ _ _ _

DZFKD

_ _ _ _ _

NVK

_ _ _

What sort of jokes do Easter chicks like?

Corny ones!

# SUPER STARS

One of these amazing starfish does not match any of the others. Can you see which one is a lone star?

**What do you use to cut the ocean in two?**
ɐ seasaw!

# TWISTER

Which tornado has scooped up numbers that add up to exactly 100?

What did the tornado say to the sports car?
"Want to go for a spin?"

55

# WE ARE SAILING

Use the grid to help you copy this picture of a Kon-Tiki style raft. Would you set sail across the ocean on such a tiny vessel?

**What did the diver shout when he swam into a seaweed forest?**
"Kelp!"

# WONDER-FALL

Mark each creature when you have found it in the large picture.

**When do monkeys fall from the sky?**
During Ape-ril showers!

57

# LEAF IT OUT

Can you see this exact pattern of leaves hidden somewhere in the large grid?

---

**What did the tree say after winter had passed?**

What a re-leaf!

58

# A BUG'S LIFE

How many new words of three or more letters can you make from the phrase below? One is there already to help get you started.

## STOP BUGGING ME!

1. BITES
2. 
3. 
4. 
5. 
6. 
7. 
8. 
9. 
10. 
11. 
12. 
13. 
14. 
15. 
16. 

**Why are cats so good at exams?**
They give purrfect answers!

# WALK THE WALK

Join the stork on his walk, following numbers from the nine times table to get through the grid to the nest. You cannot move diagonally.

| 47 | 36 | 72 | 18 | 25 | 12 |    |
|----|----|----|----|----|----|----|
| 39 | 15 | 42 | 99 | 45 | 9  |    |
| 14 | 54 | 27 | 63 | 24 | 40 | 14 |
| 28 | 45 | 58 | 18 | 48 | 63 | 6  |
| 64 | 16 | 25 | 81 | 27 | 9  | 35 |
| 32 | 55 | 80 | 28 | 72 | 56 | 16 |
| 11 | 90 | 54 | 36 | 108| 45 | 32 |
|    | 27 | 32 | 19 | 24 | 81 | 70 | 37 |

**Why are storks wiser than chickens?**
Ever heard of Kentucky Fried Stork?!

# SIREN SONG

Which of the misty mermaid silhouettes is an exact match for the picture?

**Why didn't the mermaid believe what her friends told her?**

It sounded fishy!

# BIRTHDAY BONANZA

Three children are celebrating their birthdays in the same week, but they are each doing a different activity. Who is doing what and when?

|        | Monday | Tuesday | Wednesday |
|--------|--------|---------|-----------|
| Bill   |        |         |           |
| Jill   |        |         |           |
| Will   |        |         |           |

Bill doesn't want to go skating. His birthday is not on Monday.

The person going skating has a birthday on Wednesday.

The bowling alley is closed on Monday.

Jill's birthday is on Monday.

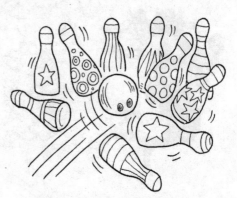

|        | Movies | Skating | Bowling |
|--------|--------|---------|---------|
| Bill   |        |         |         |
| Jill   |        |         |         |
| Will   |        |         |         |

What do they sing on your birthday in Iceland?
"Freeze a jolly good fellow!"

# LET'S EXPLORE

Which of the famous explorers below is the odd one out?

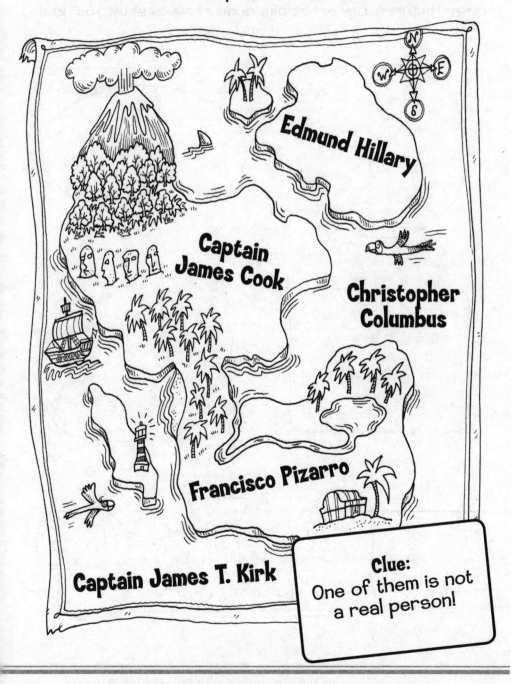

Edmund Hillary

Captain James Cook

Christopher Columbus

Francisco Pizarro

Captain James T. Kirk

Clue:
One of them is not a real person!

Who was the first European cat to discover America?
Christofur Columpuss!

63

# ALL CHANGE

Change these shapes into animals by adding legs, ears, and other features. Our artist has done some to show you how!

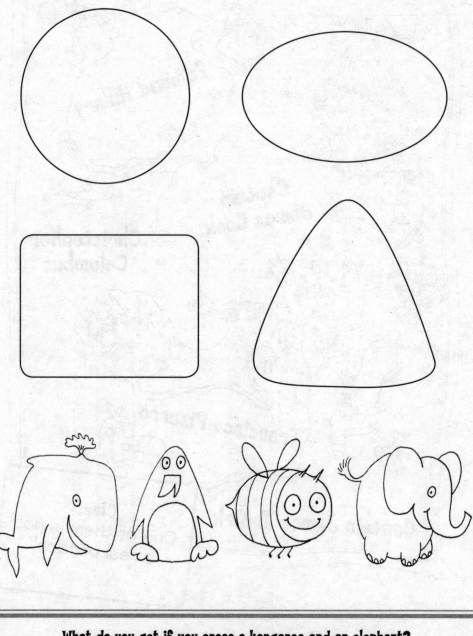

**What do you get if you cross a kangaroo and an elephant?**
Great big holes all over Australia!

64

# FLOWER POWER

Find all of the listed flowers hidden
in the grid. Pretty!

```
D A H P Y I T U L P A P
A E P A N S Y D E L P A
P M J Y A R Y S S I O N
O D U A L I O I O L P F
P L A Y S R R V P R P O
V I O H C M Y I Y T Y T
T L O H L L A L S E R U
P A B D I I V E T L T L
P C E L P A T U O P U
Y J A S M I N E L I Y N
V I O P Y E T T I V A E
H P P D A H L T P P Y R
```

**TULIP**     **PANSY**

**VIOLET**    **ROSE**

**POPPY**     **LILY**

**JASMINE**   **DAHLIA**

**LILAC**     **IRIS**

**Grandma: I hear you've been missing school?**

Jasmine: That's a lie. I haven't missed it one bit!

65

# SNAIL TRAIL

Find a path through the garden, following
the arrows in the right direction
each time.

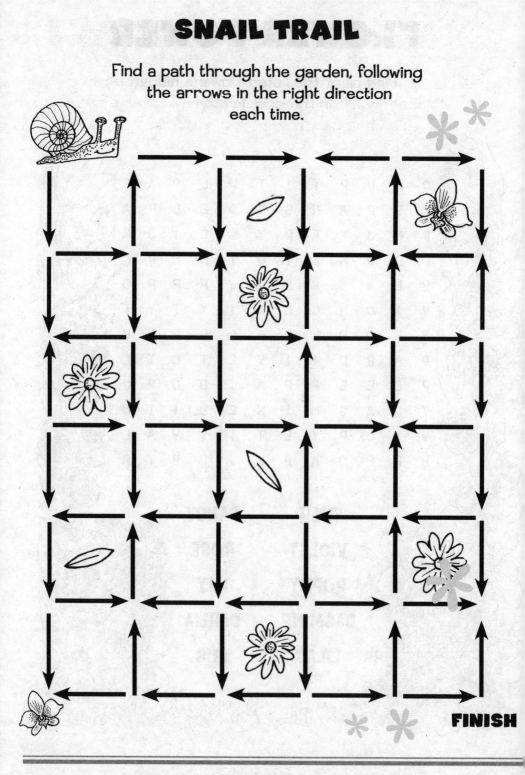

**FINISH**

**What did the snail write in the Valentine's card?**
"Be my Valen-Slime!"

# EGGS-STRAORDINARY

Did you know that parrot eggs are round, not pointed?
Find a way from the bottom of the egg maze to
the perky parrot in the middle.

**What happens when a pirate ship gets old?**
It keels over!

Use the grid references to work out the name of the deepest place in the world's oceans. Then give the code for the ocean it is in.

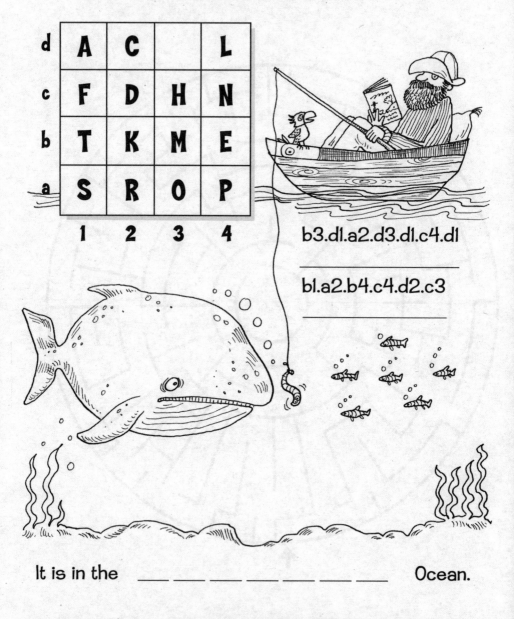

|   | 1 | 2 | 3 | 4 |
|---|---|---|---|---|
| d | A | C |   | L |
| c | F | D | H | N |
| b | T | K | M | E |
| a | S | R | O | P |

b3.d1.a2.d3.d1.c4.d1

_____

b1.a2.b4.c4.d2.c3

_____

It is in the ___ ___ ___ ___ ___ ___ ___ Ocean.

**What did the Pacific Ocean say to the Atlantic Ocean?**
Nothing, it just waved!

# IN THE HEAVENS

Add to this shooting star to make a beautiful
pattern in the night sky.

**What did one star say to another star?**
"Do you want to glow on a date?"

# SNOW PROBLEM!

What number goes in the middle of the snowflake?
(Clue: think around the problem to find the pattern.)

2

1

4

29

?

7

22

11

16

**What did one snowman say to the other?**
"Can you smell carrots?"

# IN THE WILD

Study the two pictures carefully to find eight differences between them.

**Which gorilla had six wives?**
Henry the Ape!

# FALLING TREASURE

What has fallen from the trees? Rearrange the letters in each group to find out.

a

R O N C A

b

H T N E U S T C

c

T C N E E H U B

d

N P E I O C E N

**What did the almond say to the pistachio?**

"You're nut so bad, you know!"

# HIGH JUMP

Add up the numbers for each bug to see which can jump the highest.

**a**
12  46
7  35
89

**b**
67  41
23  5
19

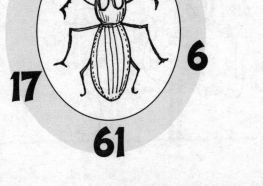

**c**
38  54
17  6
61

**d**
72  29
33  4
50

How do you get rid of an annoying wasp?
Tell it to buzz off!

73

# LEGGY LOVELIES

How many of these flamingos are standing on
one leg, not two?

**What do you call a woman with one leg on either side of a river?**
Bridget!

74

# SEA MONSTER

Use the code to figure out the name of a huge fish that changes from black and yellow to greenish-brown as it grows up.

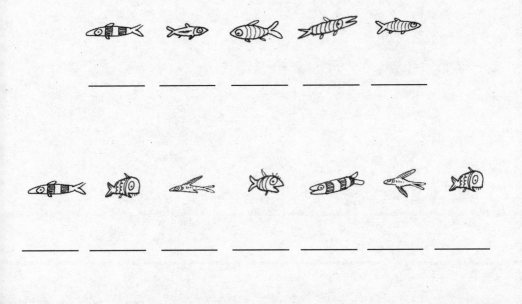

# CRYSTAL CLEAR

Each of the snowflakes has an identical match except one.
Can you find it?

**What's white and goes up?**
A stupid snowflake!

# PYRAMID PEAKS

Work out what number is missing from the third pyramid, where the ? appears.

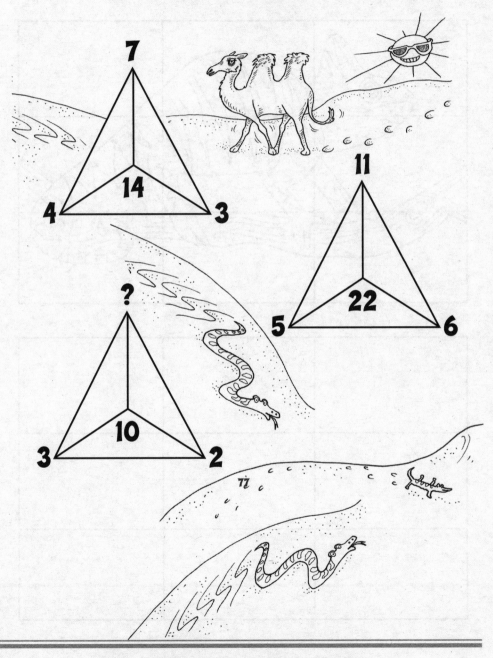

**7**

**14**

**4**   **3**

**11**

**22**

**5**   **6**

**?**

**10**

**3**   **2**

**Why is it hard to find a camel in the desert?**
Because they're well camel-flaged!

77

# CRAFTY CREATURE

Copy the picture of the chameleon using the grid to help you. What shades will you use for his skin?

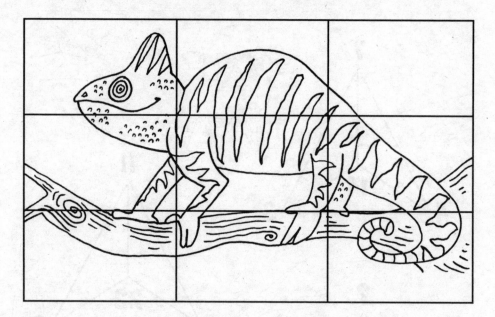

---

**What happened to the tired fairy who lay down on a branch?**

He soon dropped off!

# A PILE OF PYTHONS

How many pythons are piled up here?
Watch out for the sneaky vines
that might confuse you!

**What do you call a snake that tells tales?**
A grass snake!

# BUG-DOKU

Fill in the blanks so there is one of each funny bug in every row, column, and mini-grid.

**What do you call an ant from overseas?**
Import-ant!

# SHOWING OFF

How many new words of three or more letters can you make from the words below? One is there already to help get you started.

# BIRD OF PARADISE

1. OPERA
2. _____
3. _____
4. _____
5. _____
6. _____
7. _____
8. _____
9. _____
10. _____
11. _____
12. _____
13. _____
14. _____
15. _____
16. _____

**What animal can jump higher than the Sydney Opera House?**
All animals, because the Opera House can't jump!

# UNDERWATER ALIENS

It's said that the ocean floor is more alien to us than outer space. Study this hydrothermal vent and answer the questions.

Which numbers are from the six times table?

18   24   36   93   28   3   54

How many shells have numbers divisible by 7?

21   42   49   63   35

Which is the only number in the eight times table?

**What kind of Easter eggs do aliens have?**
Eggs-traterrestrial ones!

# CAUGHT IN A STORM

Which is the only blacked out picture
that is an exact match for
the main picture?

What should you take to avoid seasickness?
Vitamin Sea!

83

# MAP MAKING

Follow the instructions and work out which landmark goes in each numbered space on the map.

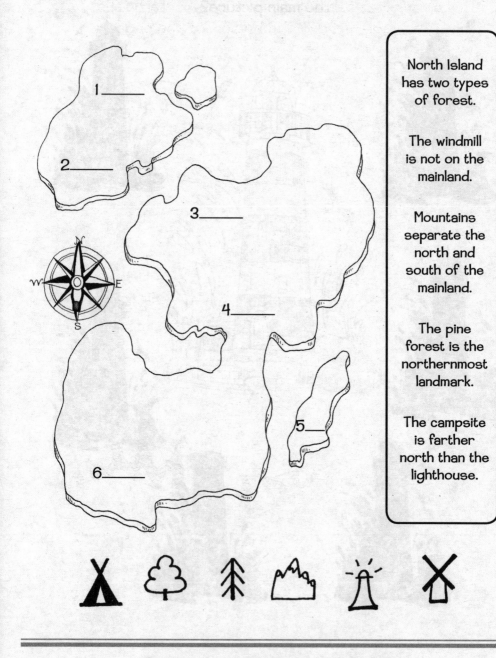

1_____

2_____

3_____

4_____

5_____

6_____

North Island has two types of forest.

The windmill is not on the mainland.

Mountains separate the north and south of the mainland.

The pine forest is the northernmost landmark.

The campsite is farther north than the lighthouse.

---

**What lives in the forest and repeats itself?**

A wild boar.

# CRAZY CREATURE

Here are some interesting facts about the animal hiding behind the rocks. To find out what it is, simply cross out every second letter in the wiggly word at the bottom of the page.

It can have poisonous skin.

It lives almost entirely in the northern hemisphere.

It can grow a new limb if one gets damaged.

It usually lays eggs.

It is an amphibian.

SNAKLIAZMIARNEDWETR

**Where do tadpoles change into frogs?**
In the croakroom!

# PLANT FOOD

Yikes! Your explorations have uncovered the world's largest carnivorous plant. What does it look like—and what is it eating?

# NICE NEST

How many times does the word WASP appear in a straight line in the grid?

**What do you call a wasp?**
A wanna-bee!

# EGG-CELLENT

Follow the eggs, pointing in the direction of the narrow end, to find a way to the puffin on the cliff top.

START

**What do dogs eat for breakfast?**
Pooched eggs!

# COMING UP

Help the submarine find a way
to the surface.

**What kind of phone does a mermaid use?**
A shell phone!

# HURRICANE HUNT

Since 1947, tropical storms have been given people's names. Use the grid references to spell the first ever name to be used.

|   | 1 | 2 | 3 | 4 |
|---|---|---|---|---|
| d | G | i | T | C |
| c | A | Y | Q | H |
| b | U | S | E | P |
| a | L | N | R | O |

c4.b1.a3.a3.d2.d4.c1.a2.b3

d1.b3.a4.a3.d1.b3

---

**Did you hear about the cow that was blown away by a tornado?**

It was an udder disaster!

# BIRD'S EYE VIEW

This hang-glider has an amazing view from up above ...
but what can she see?

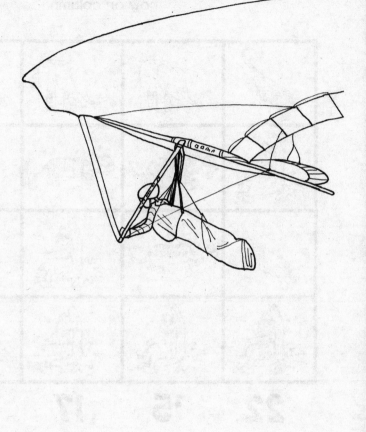

**What would you get hanging from castle walls?**
Tired arms!

# ANIMAL ADDITION

Work out the number value of each animal in the grid.
The numbers outside the grid are the sum of each
row or column.

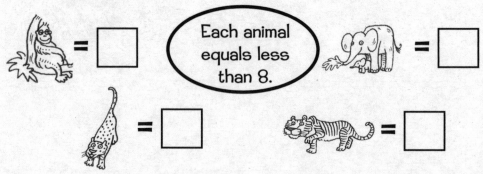

Each animal
equals less
than 8.

---

# WILD AND WONDERFUL

Try to find eight differences between these two beautiful wild scenes.

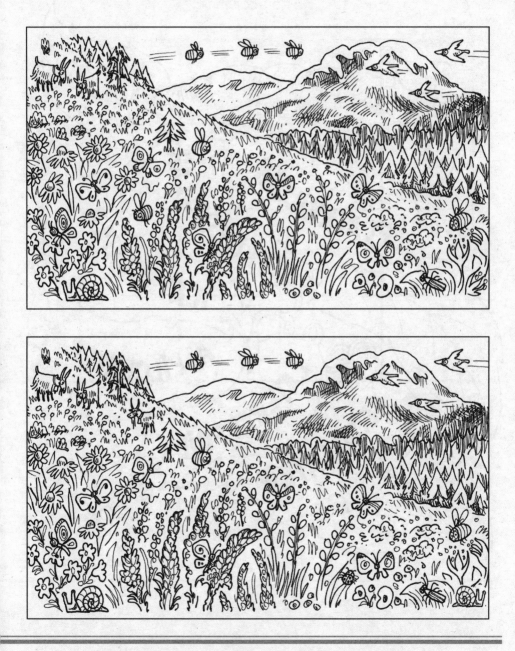

**What's the difference between a storm cloud and a bear raiding a beehive?**

One pours with rain and the other roars with pain!

# FEELING HUNGRY

Which of the groups of letters cannot be unscrambled to spell this creature's name?

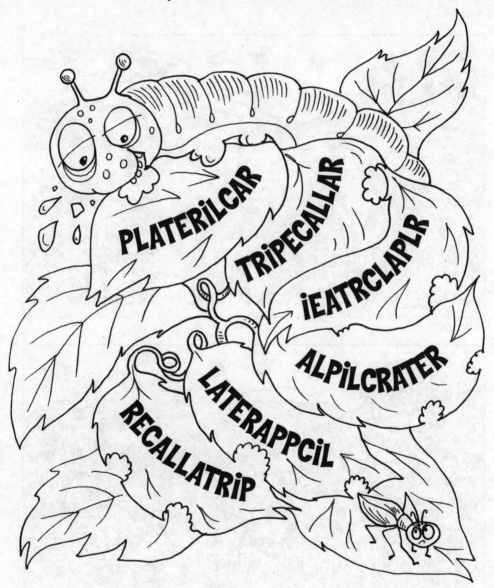

PLATERILCAR

TRIPECALLAR

iEATRCLAPLR

ALPiLCRATER

LATERAPPCiL

RECALLATRiP

**What do you call a vampire that eats all the time?**
Snackula!

94

# BIG BIRD

Ostriches are the largest birds on the planet, but which one of these has numbers that add up to the biggest total?

**a**
26  17
4  39

**b**
15  34
22  9

**c**
33  18
20  7

**d**
8  35
28  16

**Why did the pirate leave a chicken with his buried treasure?**
Because eggs marks the spot!

# ON THE ROCKS

Find one starfish that looks exactly like the one in the circle.

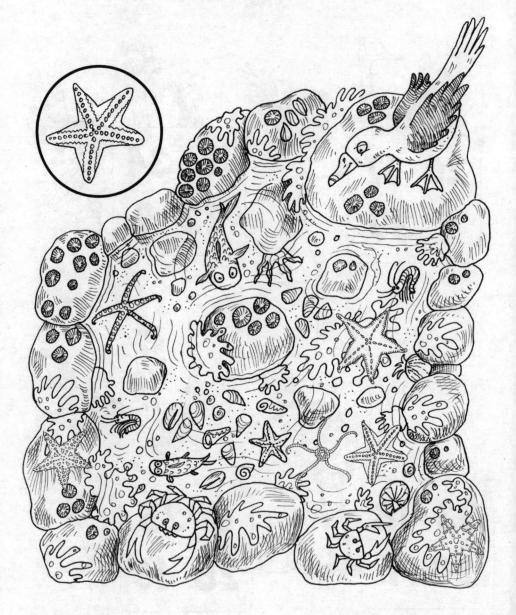

**Why wouldn't the crab twins share their rock pool?**
Because they're two shellfish!

# HIGH AND DRY

Do you know which is the driest place on Earth? Find out by replacing the numbers with letters. 1 = A, 2 = B, and so on.

$$\frac{1 . 20 . 1 . 3 . 1 . 13 . 1}{4 . 5 . 19 . 5 . 18 . 20}$$

**What would you get if you crossed a river and a desert?**
Wet and thirsty!

97

# TWO TRIBES

One of these tribal shields is slightly different from the rest. Which one is it?

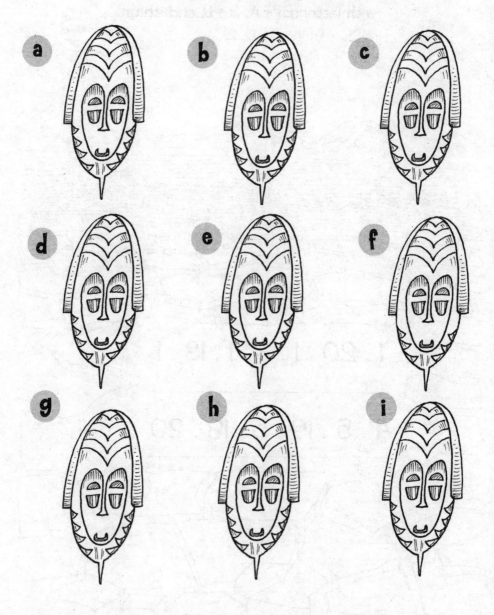

a

b

c

d

e

f

g

h

i

Who rides a horse, wears a mask, and smells good?
The Cologne Ranger!

# BIG BABY

Which baby giraffe belongs to the mother? Find the one whose numbers add up to the same total as hers.

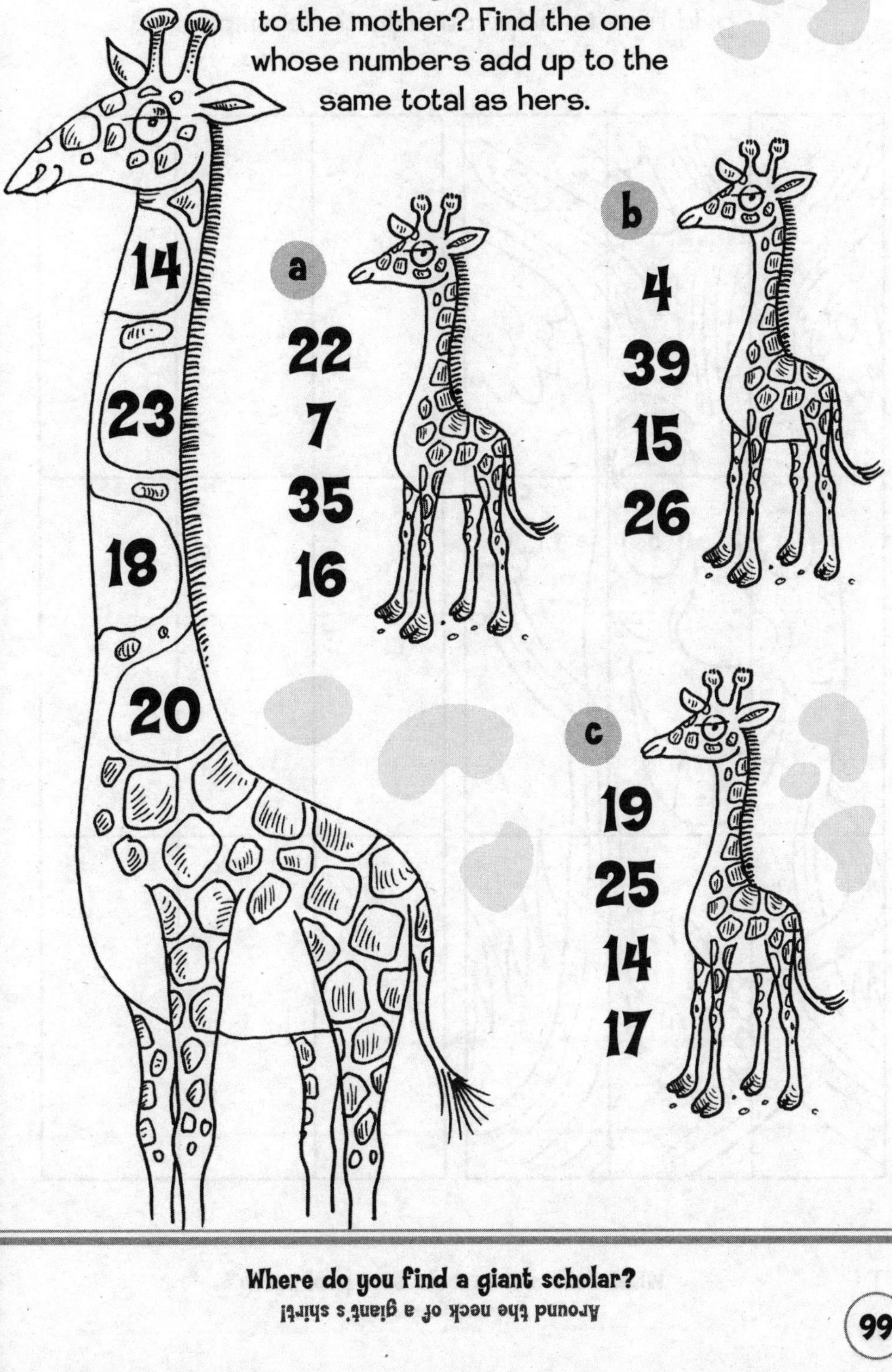

14
23
18
20

**a**
22
7
35
16

**b**
4
39
15
26

**c**
19
25
14
17

**Where do you find a giant scholar?**
Around the neck of a giant's shirt!

# DANCING TREE

Draw your own cool dancing tree character by using the grid lines to help you copy the example.

**What does a tree wear to a pool party?**
Swimming trunks!

# CREATURES COUNT

How many centipedes are scuttling around this page?

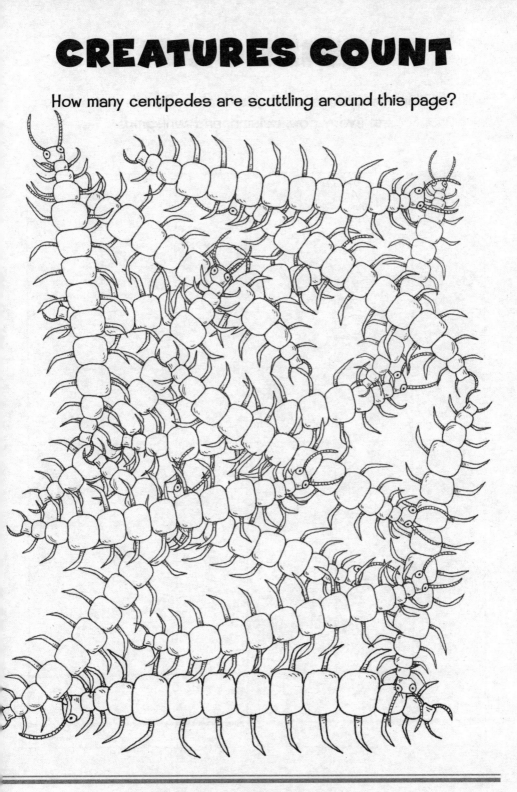

**Why is it hard to wind up a snake?**
You can't pull its leg!

# BIRDOKU

Fill in the spaces so there is one of each picture in every row, column, and mini-grid.

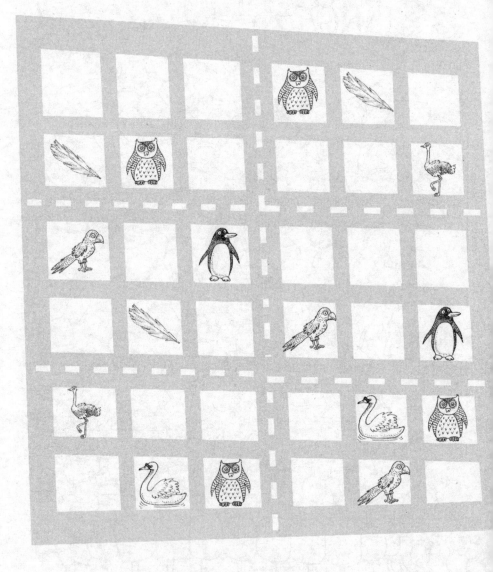

**Where do penguins go to vote?**
The South Poll!

# SAIL AWAY

How many new words of three or more letters can you make from the words below? One is there already to help.

## SAILING THE SEVEN SEAS

GALES

1. GALES
2. _____
3. _____
4. _____
5. _____
6. _____
7. _____
8. _____
9. _____
10. _____
11. _____
12. _____

**Why wouldn't the ancient Egyptian accept that her boat was sinking?**
She was in de-Nile!

# ON STRIKE

Find a way from the cloud through the raindrops to the shelter, using only numbers from the eight times table.

**What did the cloud say to the bolt of lightning?**
"You're shocking!"

# YEAR OF THE DRAGON

Which of the silhouettes is an exact match for the main picture of the majestic dragon?

**What did the dragon say when it saw Sir Lancelot?**
"Ugh, more canned food!"

# FEEDING TIME

Each animal at the zoo is fed at a different time. Jenny, Mark, and Amelie each see a different animal being fed. Who sees what, and when?

|        | Panda | Tapir | Zebra |
|--------|-------|-------|-------|
| 10am   |       |       |       |
| 1pm    |       |       |       |
| 3pm    |       |       |       |

One of the girls sees the tapir being fed.

Amelie attends the morning feeding session.

Mark misses the zebra feed at 1pm.

The panda is last to be fed.

|        | Panda | Tapir | Zebra |
|--------|-------|-------|-------|
| Jenny  |       |       |       |
| Mark   |       |       |       |
| Amelie |       |       |       |

**Why was the baby panda so spoiled?**
Because its parents panda-d to its every whim!

# POND DIPPING

Cross out any letter that appears twice, and then rearrange the letters that are left to find out what the children have caught in their net.

S T H U O D E
P M L A H U S M

Answer: _ _ _ _ _ _ _ _

---

**What do you get if you cross a dog and a frog?**
A pet that can lick you from the other side of the road!

# CAUGHT IN A TRAP

What kind of spider has spun this web? It may be
a new species, unknown to science until now!

**Have you heard the story about a poor little spider?**
It's called Spinderella!

# A RARE BIRD

The kakapo is seldom seen. It's a nocturnal, flightless parrot from New Zealand but is critically endangered. Can you find just one in the grid?

K P K K A P A K A K
P A O A O A O A K A P A
O K K A K P O A K O
K A A A K P O A A P
A K K P A O K K A A
P K A K K A P O K K
K A A O P O K A O O
A O P A K A K A P K
O P O A K A K K A P
A K A K P A K A K O

**Why are grandpa's teeth like stars?**
Because they come out at night!

(109)

# SHE SELLS SEASHELLS

Can you find a way from top to bottom, moving across or down (not diagonally), and avoiding shells with a spiral pattern?

**How did the shellfish know his kids were sick?**
They felt clammy!

# UNDER THE WEATHER

Find a way from start to finish, avoiding the bad weather along the way.

**START**

**FINISH**

**What kind of clothes do black clouds wear?**
Thunderwear!

# UNITED STATES

Reunite the two halves of each place name to find 10 US states.

KENT

RADO

ARKA

WARE

OKLA

VIRG

NOIS

NSAS

COLO

DELA

OURI

UCKY

HOMA

NEBR

MICH

ASKA

ILLI

MISS

INIA

IGAN

**What did Tennessee?**
The same thing Arkan-saw!

# NASTY GNASHERS

Eek! What creature do these giant fangs belong to?
You decide!

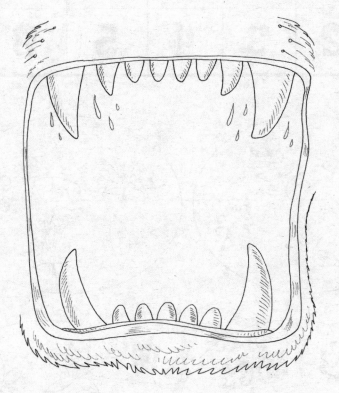

**What do vampires sing on New Year's Eve?**
Auld Fang Syne!

113

# SEASONAL SUMS

Which pile of leaves adds up to the highest answer, using the leaf code below?

| | | | | |
|---|---|---|---|---|
| 2 | 3 | 4 | 5 | 8 |

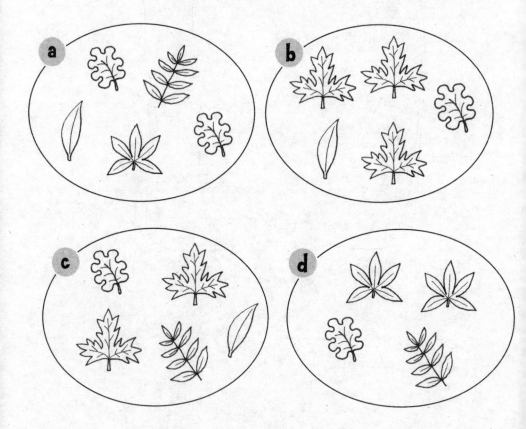

**What happened to the snowman in the spring?**
He made a pool of himself!

# BUSY BEES

Look carefully to find eight differences between these two pictures.

**Did you hear about the bee born in the spring?**
It was a May-bee!

# LOVE BIRDS

Unscramble each set of letters to find the names of six birds.

YNC AAR

HFICN

ATR RPO

INPOGEA

RLV RU ETU

AWCM

**How did the skeleton know he had found true love?**
He felt it in his bones!

# UNDER THE SEA

Work out the code to activate the airlock on this super sub.

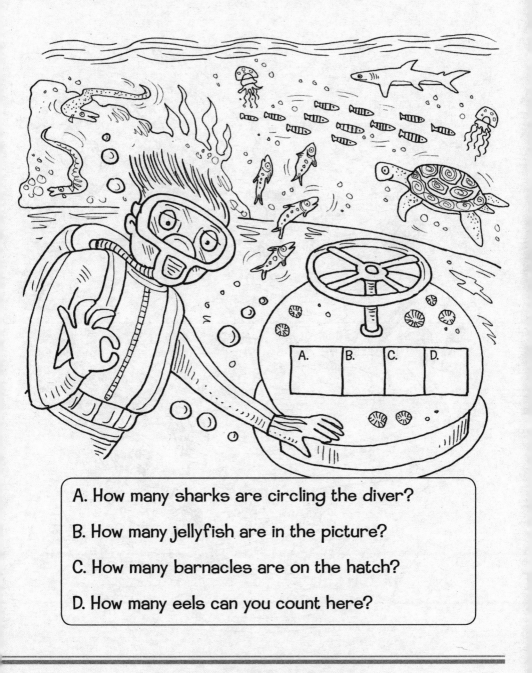

A. How many sharks are circling the diver?

B. How many jellyfish are in the picture?

C. How many barnacles are on the hatch?

D. How many eels can you count here?

**What is in the middle of a jellyfish?**
It's jellybutton!

# TORNADO TROUBLE

How many vehicles have been swept up in these tornadoes?

**What game do tornadoes play?**
Twister!

# AROUND THE WORLD

Use the code to work out the name of a great period of exploration in the fifteenth and sixteenth centuries.

**Why don't whales watch sad movies?**
It makes them blubber!

119

# SPOTTED!

Which one of the leopard's spots does not match
any of the others?

Which monarch had the worst skin?
Mary Queen of Spots!

# SQUIRREL SQUARES

Work out which symbol represents the mathematical signs +, -, x, and ÷ to make the equations work properly. The equations go across and down.

| 8 | [acorn] | 12 | [conker] | 7 | = | 13 |
|---|---|---|---|---|---|---|
| [acorn] | | [pinecone] | | [acorn] | | |
| 11 | [acorn] | 4 | [conker] | 6 | = | 9 |
| [conker] | | [pinecone] | | [acorn] | | |
| 5 | [sprig] | 1 | [sprig] | 2 | = | 10 |
| = | | = | | = | | |
| 14 | | 3 | | 15 | | |

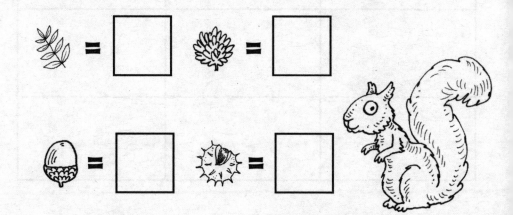

[sprig] = ☐    [pinecone] = ☐

[acorn] = ☐    [conker] = ☐

---

**How do you describe an acorn?**

In a nutshell, it's an oak tree!

# MAKE A MANTIS

Learn to draw a praying mantis by copying this one, using the grid squares to help you.

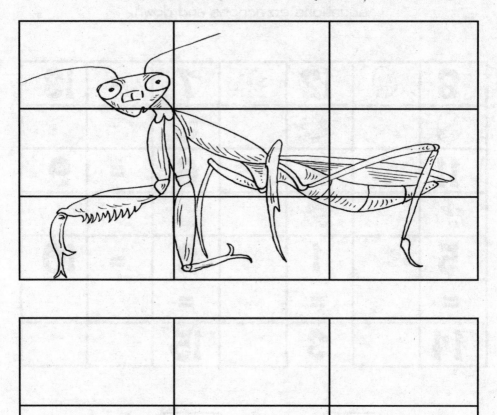

---

**What do you call a boomerang that doesn't come back?**
A stick!

# BUSY BIRDS

Tiny weaver birds build elaborate nests that are one of the biggest things made by any bird. Which are there more of here—nests or birds?

**Where do you find the best egg jokes?**
In a yolk book!

# THREE IN A ROW

Can you find three identical seashells in a row,
looking up, across, or diagonally?

---

**What's the best way to cross the ocean?**
By taxi-crab!

# A SUNNY OUTLOOK

How many new words of three or more letters can you make from the phrase below? One is there already to help get you started.

# GOOD MORNING SUNSHINE

1. SINGING
2. _____
3. _____
4. _____
5. _____
6. _____
7. _____
8. _____
9. _____
10. _____
11. _____
12. _____
13. _____
14. _____
15. _____
16. _____

What's brown, hairy, and wears sunglasses?

A coconut at the beach!

# THE GREAT DIVIDE

Cross out the numbers that are the answers
to each question. Which number are
you left with?

45

Prime numbers?                    67

63          Numbers divisible by 9?        48

7       Numbers with 6 as a factor?

12

27

29       36       22

5

13

18       54       41

**Why did the snake cross the desert?**
To get to the other sssside!

# MEET THE MEERKATS

Which of the silhouettes is an exact match for this cute group of meerkats?

# NATURE LOVER

Which t-shirt does Stacey buy from the Nature Park gift shop?

It has short sleeves.

The animal on it doesn't have prickles.

The picture is of a mammal.

The creature on it doesn't live in trees.

What's the difference between an angry rabbit and a forged banknote?
One is a mad bunny, and the other is bad money!

# BUGGING OUT

Work out which letter is not needed each time, and cross it out to reveal the names of six creepy crawlies. The first one has been done to show you how.

CRATBERBPIBLBLARB

NGLNOWWNORMN

LCLOCKLLROLACH

DURAUGUONUFULY

ACAENATAIPEADEA

MOCSQUICTOC

What did the Golden Snitch say when Harry Potter was bitten by a mosquito?

Quidd-itching!

129

# BEAUTIFUL BIRDS

Birds come in all shapes and sizes, depending on their diet and habitat. Add beaks, legs, tails, and wings to these, then finish them with bright patterns.

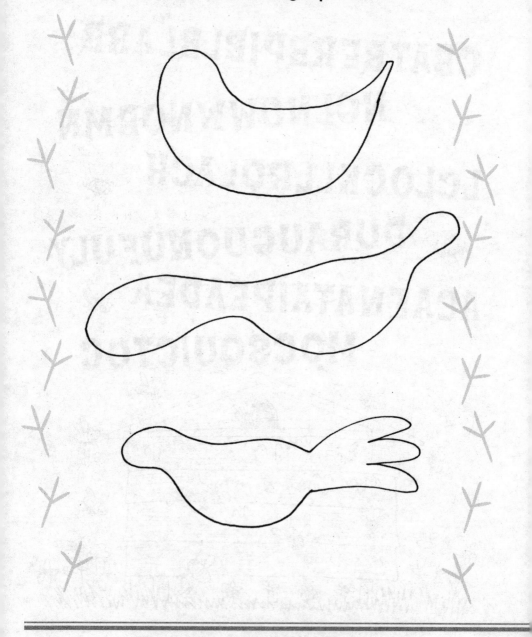

**How can you tell a worm's head from its tail?**
Tickle the middle, and see which end laughs!

# CLUELESS CREATURES

There are plenty of fish in the sea, but there are also many creatures that aren't fish. See if you can find 14 in the grid.

```
R  A  D  C  H  R  S  P  O  N  G  E
R  D  N  W  H  A  L  E  L  D  P  T
W  O  E  E  S  D  D  R  O  A  M  U
A  F  B  E  M  S  C  B  B  X  H  R
L  I  A  I  A  O  E  R  S  D  R  T
R  L  D  M  R  R  N  E  T  Y  H  L
U  E  O  A  A  M  O  E  E  B  S  E
S  R  L  R  C  L  A  M  R  U  W  S
A  R  C  A  S  A  N  S  C  R  A  E
M  U  A  H  D  O  L  P  H  I  N  T
C  R  A  B  I  P  O  Y  S  T  E  R
E  K  R  E  A  N  I  D  I  U  Q  S
```

**Why was the sea creature worried about her son?**

Because he was a crazy, mixed up squid!

# FOLLOW MY LEMUR

Find a way through the grid of compasses, following in the direction of the needle each time. See if you can catch up with the lemur!

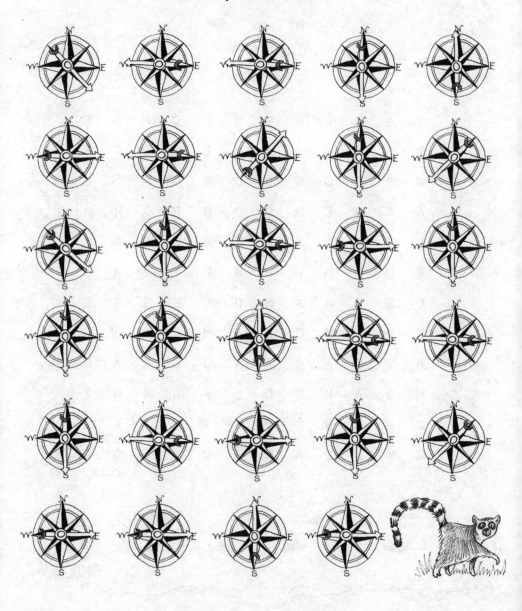

**In which direction do you head to find chocolate eggs?**

A little Easter here!

# WHITEOUT!

Help the little girl track down the Yeti in the snow. Will anyone believe her when she tells them who she met?

**What do you call a stranded polar bear?**
Ice-olated!

# CRAZY CREATURES

Ever heard of a chimpceros? Not surprising, as it doesn't exist! Rearrange these word halves to make six real creatures.

CHIMP  CEROS

WILDE  HILLA

RHINO  BURRA

SALAM  ANZEE

KOOKA  BEEST

CHINC  ANDER

What has big ears, four legs, and a trunk?

A mouse with its luggage.

# GOING UNDERGROUND

What creature do you think makes its home in this spooky cave?

Florence: Why do you only play baseball at night?
Peter: I have a vampire bat.

135

# BEING BUGGED

Solve the clues and write the number next to the correct picture. Once they're all in the right place, each row, column, and diagonal should add up to 15.

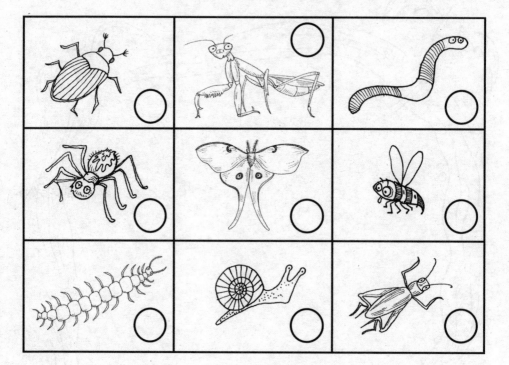

1. Watch out, it stings!

2. It has six legs

3. It carries its home around

4. It has legs on each body segment

5. A giant flying insect

6. It has no legs at all

7. It might eat its mate

8. Great at jumping

9. Two too many legs to be an insect!

---

# ALL TOGETHER NOW

Look carefully at the two pictures to spot ten differences between them.

**What do birds do on Halloween?**

They go trick-or-tweeting!

The letters A, B, and C are missing from these names. Work out which symbol represents which letter, and what the names all are.

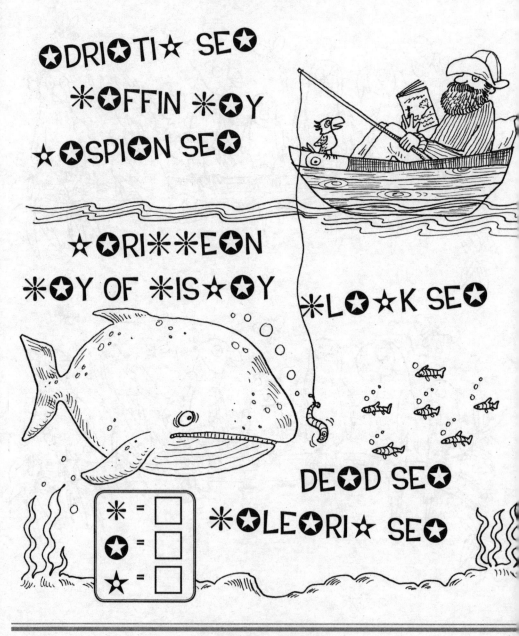

◉DRI◉TI☆ SE◉

✳OFFIN ✳◉Y

☆◉SPI◉N SE☆

☆◉RI✳✳E◉N

✳◉Y OF ✳IS☆◉Y

✳LO☆K SE◉

DE◉D SE◉

✳◉LE◉RI☆ SE◉

✳ = ☐
◉ = ☐
☆ = ☐

**Why do whales sing?**
Because they can't talk!

# LIGHTNING STRIKES

Add up the numbers in the windows to find out which building has been struck the most times.

**a** 6.4 7.6 8.3 9.1 2.1 4.5

**b** 8.9 4.3 6.8 7.2 5.7 3.1

**c** 2.4 8.8 5.7 9.5 4.5 6.1

# DESERTED

Which of the squares can NOT be found in the main picture?

**What did the weatherwoman use to curl her hair?**
A heat wave!

# WILD THING

If A = 1, B = 2, and so on, translate the message to find out who this cuddly creature is, plus some amazing facts about it.

9.20  9.19  3.1.12.12.5.4  1  16.12.1.20.25.16.21.19

9.20  8.1.19  22.5.14.15.13.15.21.19
19.20.9.14.7.5.18.19  15.14  9.20.19  6.5.5.20

9.20  9.19  1  13.1.13.13.1.12
2.21.20  12.1.25.19  5.7.7.19

15.14.12.25  20.8.5  2.1.2.9.5.19
8.1.22.5  20.5.5.20.8

# FLUTTERBY

All of these butterflies can be found in the mountain scene—
except one. Which one isn't there?

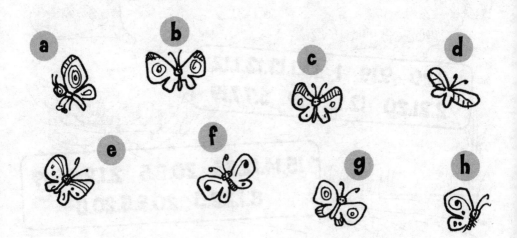

**What was the highest mountain before Everest was discovered?**
Still Mount Everest!

# A REAL STINGER

Are you ready for some kooky calculations?
Work out what number fills each blank space.
Use the top rows as an example.

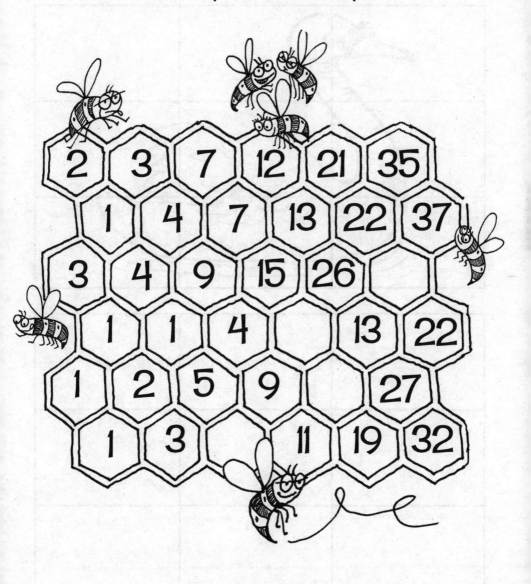

| 2 | 3 | 7 | 12 | 21 | 35 |
|---|---|---|----|----|----|
| 1 | 4 | 7 | 13 | 22 | 37 |
| 3 | 4 | 9 | 15 | 26 |    |
| 1 | 1 | 4 |    | 13 | 22 |
| 1 | 2 | 5 | 9  | 27 |    |
| 1 | 3 |   | 11 | 19 | 32 |

What gift did the smelly bee receive from its friends?
Bee-odorant!

143

# SWIMMING SWAN

Draw your own swan, using the grid to
help you copy this one.

# SURF'S UP

Mark each item when you have found it in the large picture.

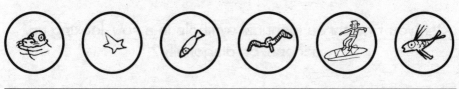

**What do you need to drive your car along the beach?**
Four-eel drive!

# WHATEVER THE WEATHER

Can you find three identical symbols in a row, looking up, across, or diagonally?

**What's the difference between weather and climate?**

You can't weather a tree, but you can climate!

# SIGHTSEEING

How many new words of three or more letters can you make from the phrase below? One is there already to help get you started.

# WONDERS OF THE WORLD

1. FOREST
2. _____
3. _____
4. _____
5. _____
6. _____
7. _____
8. _____
9. _____
10. _____

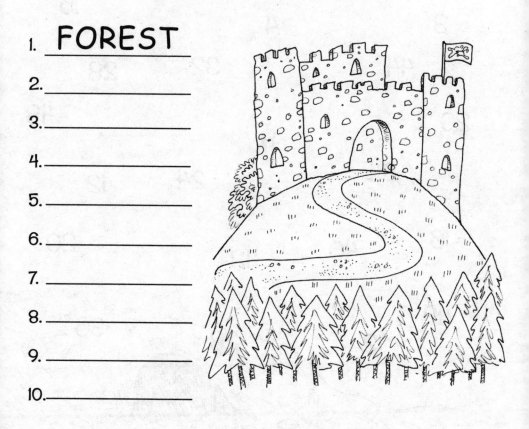

**Why did soldiers fire arrows from the castle?**
They were trying to get their point across!

147

# WANDERING WOMBATS

Which wombat can find a way home using every leaf and only numbers from the four times table?

**a**

**b**

**c**

16

8    4

44    32    28

20    48

8

34    24    12

16    40    42    20

48    36

12    28

---

**What's purple and fishy and found off the coast of Australia?**

The Grape Barrier Reef!

# BLAST ZONE

Which of the shadowy volcanoes is an exact match for the picture in the middle?

**Why should you never argue on a hot-air balloon ride?**
You don't want to fall out!

# WHO GOES THERE?

Use the clues to work out which person finds each bug, and where each creature is lurking. No two are in the same place!

|  | Beetle | Moth | Centipede |
|---|---|---|---|
| Amy |  |  |  |
| Ben |  |  |  |
| Charlie |  |  |  |

The centipede is not near a branch.

Amy finds her creature in a tree.

Ben finds a creature that can't fly.

The moth is not in a tree.

|  | Beetle | Moth | Centipede |
|---|---|---|---|
| Rock |  |  |  |
| Tree |  |  |  |
| Hedge |  |  |  |

---

**What's the largest moth in the world?**

A mammoth!

# THINK PINK

Cross out any letter that appears more than once and use the remaining letters to spell the food that gives flamingos their distinctive plumage.

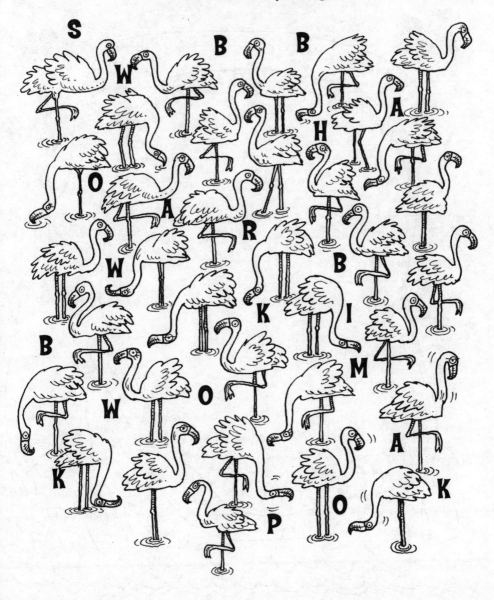

**Where do American banshees go on school trips?**
Lake Eerie!

151

# SWALLOWED!

What is this whale gobbling from the ocean?
Fish and ships, or maybe something that's
more of a treat? You decide!

**What is the saddest creature in the ocean?**
The blue whale!

# STICK WITH IT

How many hockey sticks are there in this muddle?

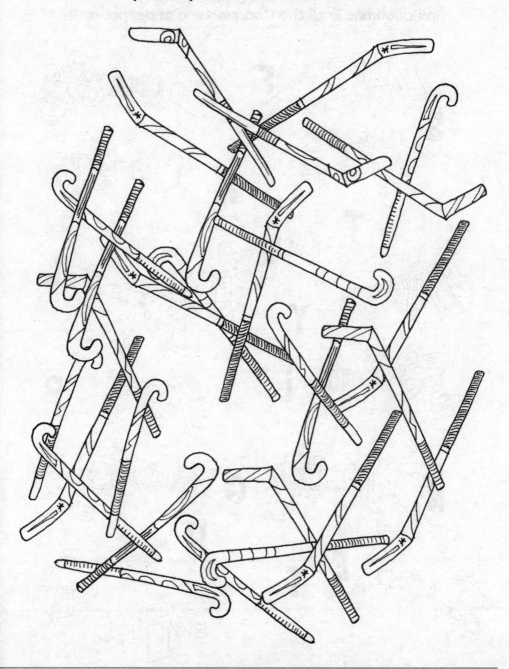

**Why did dad take his razor to sports day?**
He wanted to shave a few seconds off his time!

# SUPER SHOOTERS

Use the letters only from the guns shooting to the left to find out what Krall the Conqueror's superpower is.

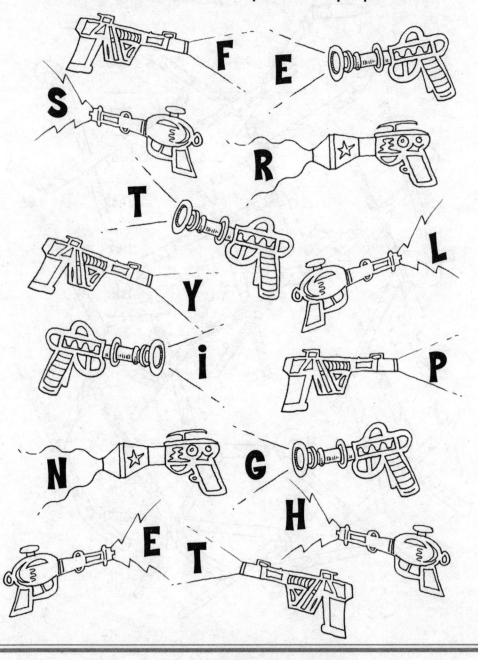

**How many planets are out in space?**
All of them!

# JUST JOKING

Follow the instructions to find the answer to the joke.

## Why are cats good at video games?

| so | when | because | they |
|---|---|---|---|
| kick | squeak | should | always |
| save | have | with | back |
| twenty | stick | nine | lick |
| clock | lives | paws | whiskers |

1. Get rid of words that begin with S.
2. Cross out any word with W in it.
3. Don't use words ending in K.

How can you tell if a cat likes the rain?

Because when it rains, it purrs!

# CIAO ITALIA!

Julia is visiting Italy to see the famous sights. Work out which letters are missing from the alphabet at each landmark to find out which cities she goes to.

BCDEFGHJKLMN
OQRTUVWXYZ

ABCDFGHIJKLNP
QSTUVWXYZ

BCDEFGHJKOPQ
RSTUVWXYZ

BCDFGHIJKMOQ
RTUVWXYZ

**Why was it so hot in Ancient Rome?**
Because of all the gladi-radiators!

156

# POWWOW, NOW!

A powwow gives Native Americans the chance to dance and celebrate in a traditional way. Look at the main picture and see which of the shadows matches it, as night begins to fall.

**What do you call a Native American ghost?**
Poca-haunt-us!

# DREAM TEAM

Design a logo for your top team. Base it on their real one, or make up one of your own.

---

**Why was Cinderella thrown off the football team?**
Because she kept running away from the ball!

# EAGLE EYES

See if you can find the smaller squares somewhere in the main picture. Write the grid reference for each one.

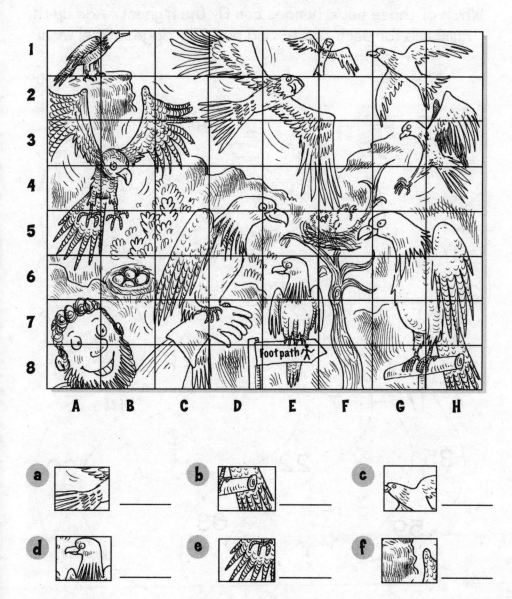

**Did you know that I can cut down a tree just by staring at it?**
It's true—I saw it with my own eyes!

159

# BETTER, FASTER, HIGHER

Which of these superheroes can fly the highest? Add up the numbers for each one to find out. The biggest total wins!

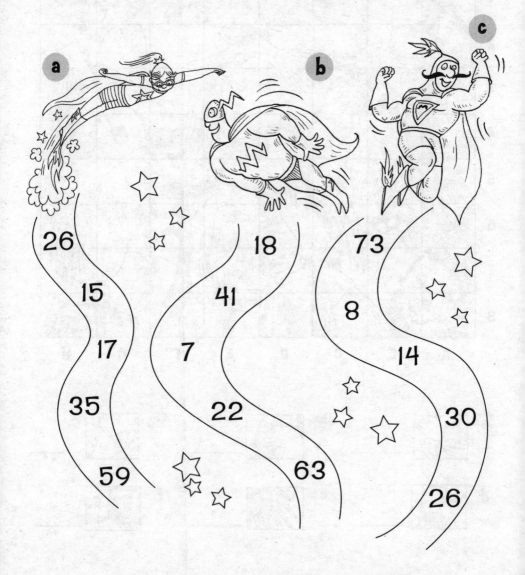

a
26
15
17
35
59

b
18
41
7
22
63

c
73
8
14
30
26

**What can you see flying through the sky on Christmas Eve?**
A U.F. Ho-Ho-Ho!

160

# IT'S A MYSTERY

There are 20 pets hidden in this wordsearch grid, but no clues to help you find them! Look for them up and down, across, and diagonally.

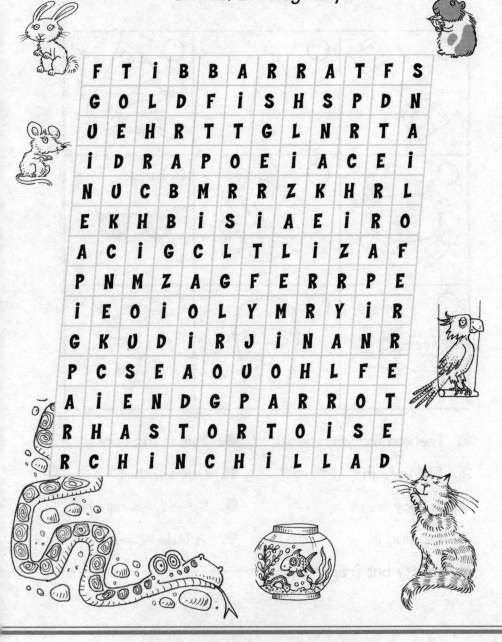

|   |   |   |   |   |   |   |   |   |   |   |
|---|---|---|---|---|---|---|---|---|---|---|
| F | T | i | B | B | A | R | R | A | T | F | S |
| G | O | L | D | F | i | S | H | S | P | D | N |
| U | E | H | R | T | T | G | L | N | R | T | A |
| i | D | R | A | P | O | E | i | A | C | E | i |
| N | U | C | B | M | R | R | Z | K | H | R | L |
| E | K | H | B | i | S | i | A | E | i | R | O |
| A | C | i | G | C | L | T | L | i | Z | A | F |
| P | N | M | Z | A | G | F | E | R | R | P | E |
| i | E | O | i | O | L | Y | M | R | Y | i | R |
| G | K | U | D | i | R | J | i | N | A | N | R |
| P | C | S | E | A | O | U | O | H | L | F | E |
| A | i | E | N | D | G | P | A | R | R | O | T |
| R | H | A | S | T | O | R | T | O | i | S | E |
| R | C | H | i | N | C | H | i | L | L | A | D |

**What is stranger than seeing a cat fish?**
Seeing a goldfish bowl!

161

# FUN IN THE SUN

Work out which clue describes each item and write the number in the right square. All of the rows, columns, and diagonals should add up to 15.

1. Fashion for your face

2. Flying high

3. A juicy treat

4. Digging it!

5. Pretty but fragile

6. Yum in the sun!

7. Goes with 4

8. Speedy swimmers

9. A little nipper

---

**What do horses wear at the beach?**
Clip-clops!

# PICK A POLE

Which of these totem poles is the odd one out?

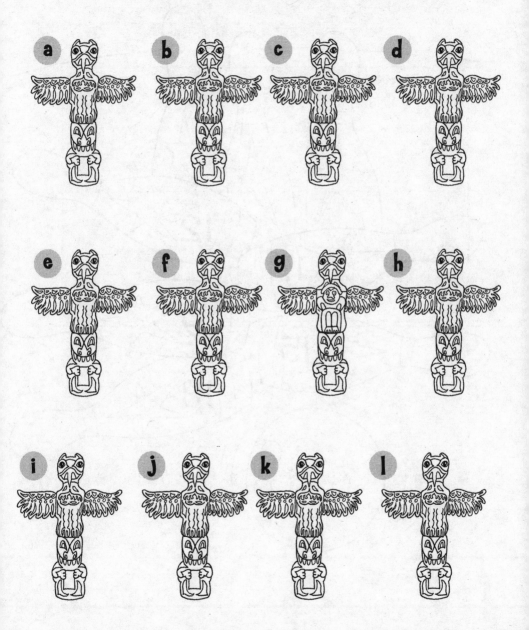

**In which American state can you buy tiny drinks?**
Mini-soda!

# BOWLED OVER

Add up the scores on the pins to find out the total score.

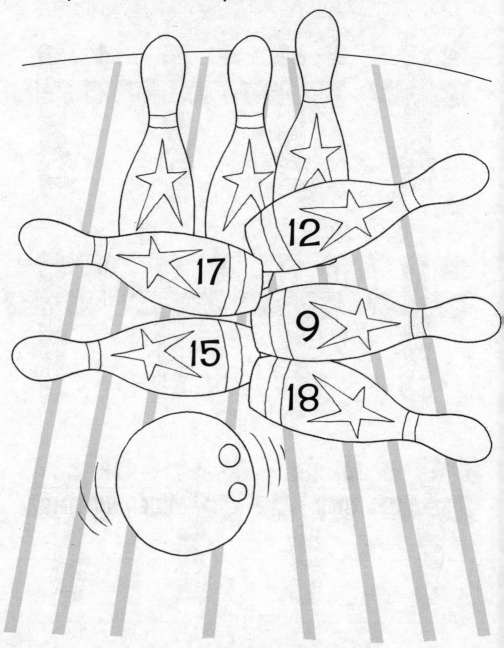

**Why didn't the ghost try to win a cuddly toy?**
He didn't have a ghost of a chance!

# TIME TO EAT!

Use the letters on the clock face to work out which zoo animals are expecting their food at the times shown. Follow the instructions in the box.

Write down the letters shown by the minute hand, then by the hour hand, for each time. The letters will spell an animal's name. For example, quarter to five = LION.

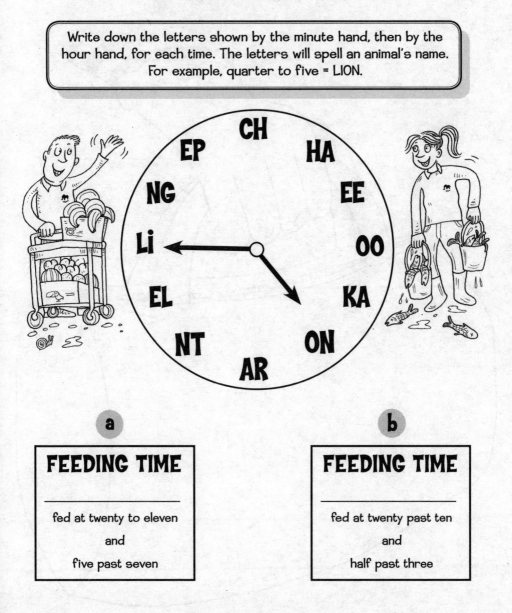

### a

## FEEDING TIME

_____

fed at twenty to eleven

and

five past seven

### b

## FEEDING TIME

_____

fed at twenty past ten

and

half past three

# X-RAY VISION

Imagine you are a superhero with X-ray eyes. That's right, you can see right through things! What is this bad guy carrying in his bag?

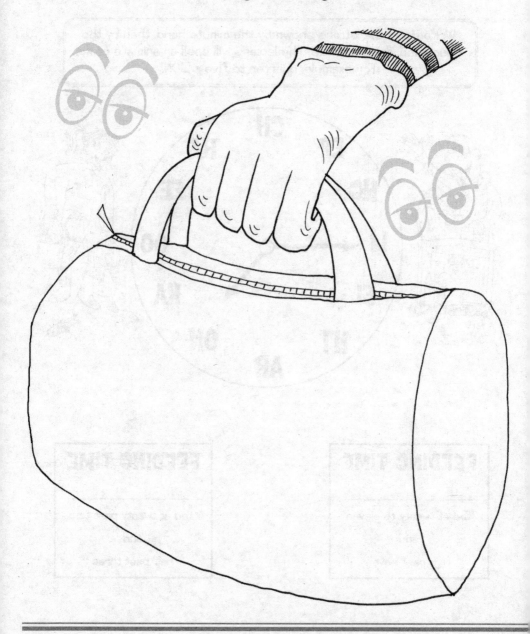

**Stacey: I was given x-rays by my dentist yesterday.**
Casey: Oh, tooth pics?

# MUCKING OUT

Ferdy loves her pony so much, she doesn't even mind mucking out! Can you find ten carrots hidden in and around the stables?

**Why did the cowboy ride a horse?**
It was too heavy to carry!

# ON THE CASE

Helen has forgotten the code to open her suitcase. Can you help her to work it out?

1. Days in May minus days in June
2. Legs on a flamingo times number of blind mice
3. Hours in a day divided by half a dozen
4. Legs on a spider minus Goldilocks' bears

---

**How did Vikings send secret messages?**
They used Norse code!

# THE OLD WEST

Cross out any letter that appears more than once.
The letters that are left will spell the name of a true
cowboy state of the USA.

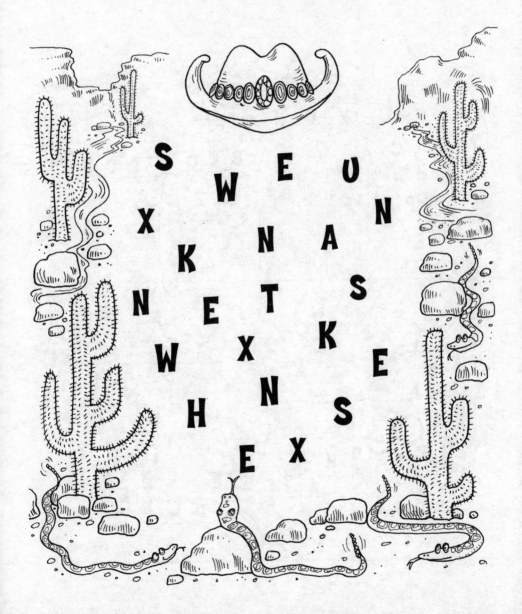

# ON YOUR BIKE

Circle every third letter on the mountain bike track to discover a type of cycling, sometimes known as XC.

---

**What is the hardest thing when you learn to ride a bike?**
The ground!

170

# BIRD BRAINS

Find all 25 feathered friends in this giant wordsearch grid.

| E | A | L | B | A | T | R | O | S | S | E | P | C | P |
|---|---|---|---|---|---|---|---|---|---|---|---|---|---|
| H | M | W | O | O | D | W | T | O | U | C | H | T | I |
| W | E | U | C | U | L | C | K | O | O | A | E | H | G |
| E | R | R | H | O | R | N | B | I | L | L | A | R | E |
| A | P | E | N | G | U | I | N | P | W | B | S | U | O |
| G | E | N | N | G | R | E | B | E | E | I | A | S | N |
| L | K | I | O | B | P | E | L | I | C | A | N | H | I |
| E | O | S | T | R | I | C | H | P | E | D | T | T | B |
| W | O | O | D | P | E | C | K | E | R | H | O | U | O |
| O | K | R | O | B | D | H | R | T | R | O | U | V | R |
| R | C | D | T | U | R | K | E | Y | B | R | C | W | E |
| C | U | U | C | P | A | R | R | O | T | N | A | R | E |
| A | C | K | A | L | B | F | L | A | M | I | N | G | O |

| | | | | |
|---|---|---|---|---|
| TOUCAN | HERON | PHEASANT | PELICAN | WREN |
| HORNBILL | OWL | ALBATROSS | PIGEON | ROBIN |
| OSTRICH | EAGLE | GREBE | DOVE | CROW |
| KIWI | EMU | PENGUIN | PARROT | THRUSH |
| WOODPECKER | DUCK | FLAMINGO | CUCKOO | TURKEY |

**Which owl robbed the rich to give to the poor?**

Robin Hoot!

# JEWEL THIEF

Which adversary does the Blue Comet find himself up against this time? Use the code key to find out.

What kind of jewels did ancient Egyptians decorate their coffins with?
Tomb-stones!

# DOG TIRED

This pet pup has worn itself out! Look carefully on its bed to find one shape that is different from all the rest.

**How much does a slobbery dog love its owner?**
Drooly, madly, deeply!

173

# YOU'RE IN CHARGE

Imagine you're the ruler of your own country. What would your flag, money, and stamps look like?

**How do mermaids make a decision?**

They flipper coin!

# HOME, SWEET HOME

Find each of the pieces in the main picture below, and write down the correct grid reference for each.

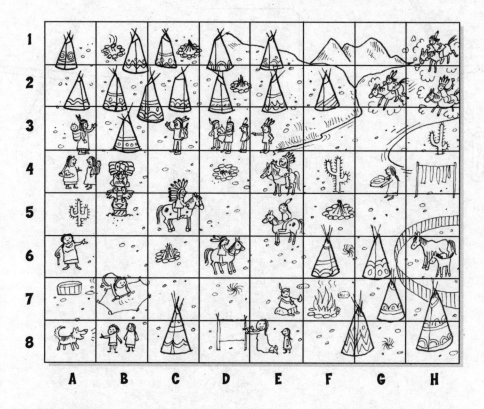

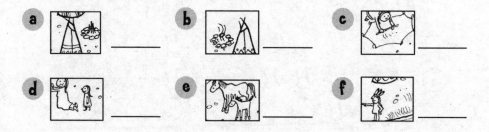

**Why shouldn't you worry if you see mice in your home?**
They're probably doing the mousework!

175

# ALL THE BALLS

The mini-grid appears only once in the whole
of the larger grid. Can you find it?

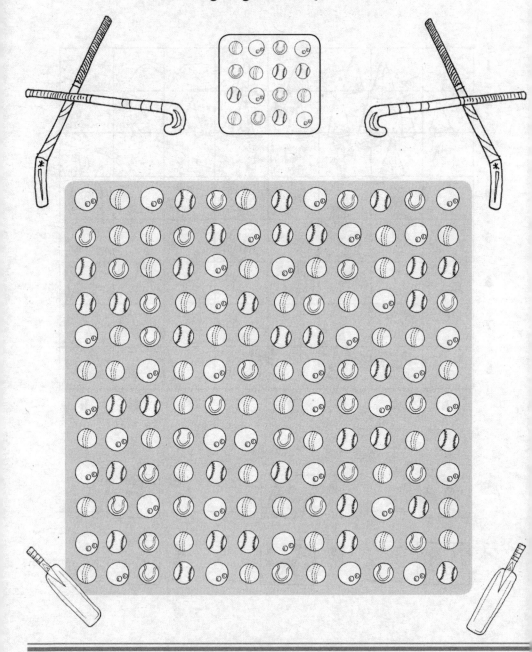

# ROLL UP, ROLL UP!

How many armadillos are there on this page? Some of them have rolled up in a ball to hide, but you should still count them!

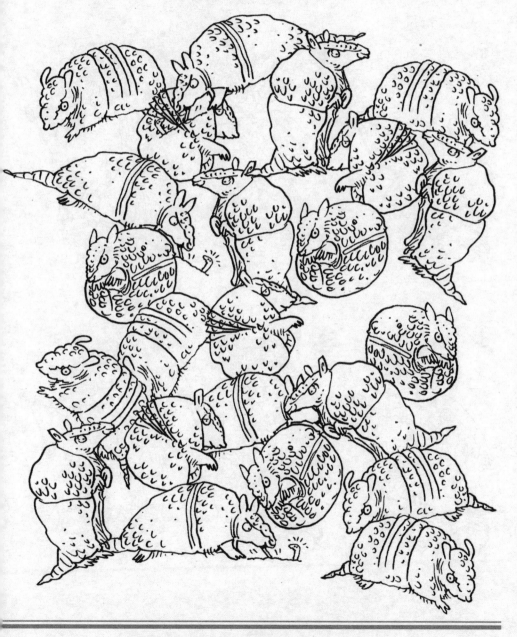

**Why wasn't the armadillo stressed?**
He always just rolled with it.

# UNDERWATER RESCUE

When things go wrong in the water, you need Aqua Girl!
Which two of these superhero pictures are the same?

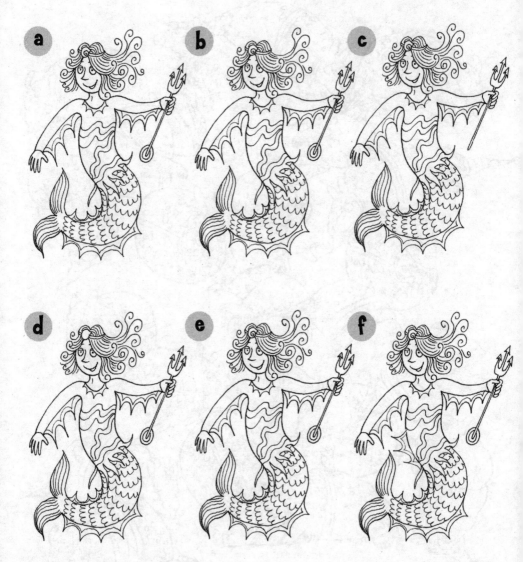

**Why did the merman stop reading a book about an electric eel?**
It was too shocking!

# FUNNY BUNNIES

Which of the jigsaw pieces finishes the picture of the cutest bunnies you could wish to see?

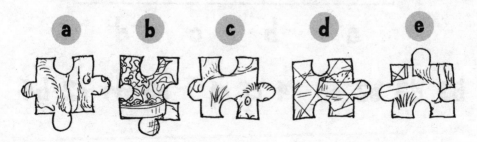

a   b   c   d   e

---

**What do you call a man with rabbits in his pockets?**
Warren!

# DREAM TICKET

Use the grid references to write down the correct letters.
They will spell out the place where the Martinez family are
going this summer.

| | a | b | c | d |
|---|---|---|---|---|
| **4** | R | S | i | E |
| **3** | K | F | N | L |
| **2** | O | W | Y | U |
| **1** | A | G | D | M |

b3 d3 a2 a4 c4 c1 a1    a3 d4 c2 b4

___ ___ ___ ___ ___ ___ ___    ___ ___ ___ ___

---

**Why did Humpty Dumpty have a great fall?**
To make up for a miserable summer!

# SADDLE UP

Help the cowgirl find her way through the desert and ride into town for the rodeo.

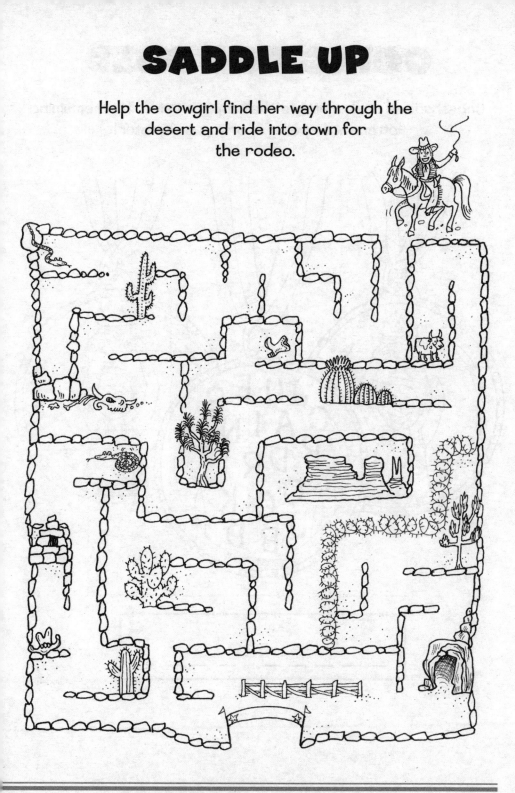

**Why did the cowgirl choose her horse in daytime?**
She didn't want nightmares!

# GOING FOR GOLD

Cross out all of the letters that appear twice. The remaining letters will spell a sporting superstar!

_ _ _ _ _   _ _ _ _

# HILARIOUS HYBRID

What do you think it would look like if you crossed a lion with a rhino? Or an ostrich with a penguin? Draw your silliest idea here and give it a name.

## ROLL UP!
### COME AND SEE THE INCREDIBLE
_____ !

What do you get if you cross a vampire and a circus performer?
Someone who goes straight for the juggler!

183

# BOO! HISS!

The evil Doc Paradox has cloned himself, but one of the clones has gone slightly wrong. Which one is different from all the rest?

Chloe: How come you're so good at tennis?
Zoe: It's not racket science!

# CUDDLY CREATURES

Study the map of the urban zoo and use it to answer the questions.

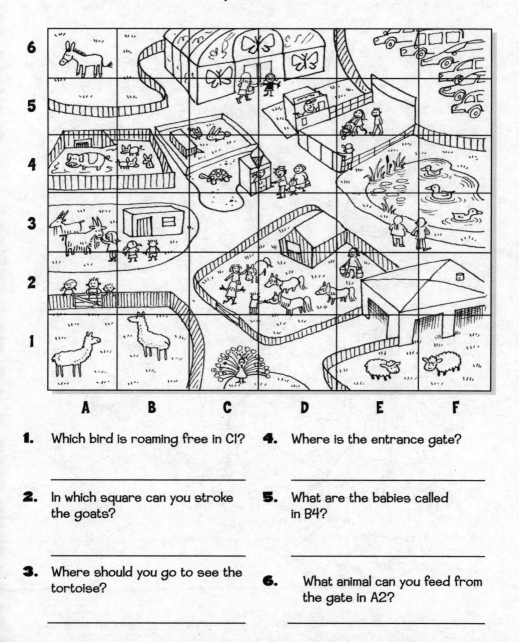

1. Which bird is roaming free in C1?

   _____

2. In which square can you stroke the goats?

   _____

3. Where should you go to see the tortoise?

   _____

4. Where is the entrance gate?

   _____

5. What are the babies called in B4?

   _____

6. What animal can you feed from the gate in A2?

   _____

**What did the pig farmer give his wife on Valentine's Day?**
Hogs and kisses!

# GET PACKING

Help Luisa find ten items that go together to make five pairs. The other things are staying behind!

**What does Grumpy pack in his lunchbox?**
Sour grapes!

# THE LONE RANGER

Can you find the word RANGER hidden just once in this grid?
Look across, up and down, and diagonally.

R A N G G E R E E G
A R E G A N A N R A
N A N G R A N A A G
E N A E N E N G N R
R A R R G A E A R E
A A E A E G R A N G
R E G A N G R A N R
E G N E E G A E G E
R A G E R N E N E E
G R E G A N A R G N

What do you call a man who lives wild with a pack of wolves?
Wolfgang!

187

# SPORTS SQUARE

Work out which clue describes each item and write the number in the right square. All of the rows, columns, and diagonals should add up to 15.

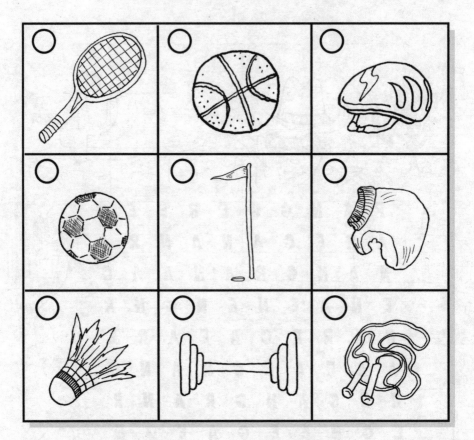

**1.** You wanna fight?

**2.** A sport with aces

**3.** Heavy, man!

**4.** Light as a feather

**5.** A hole in one?

**6.** Head case!

**7.** Slam dunk

**8.** Give it a twirl

**9.** Back of the net!

---

**Casey: Why is your sister so good at sport?**
Stacey: She has athlete's foot!

# LION LAUGHS

Follow the instructions to find the answer to the joke.

## What did the lion say when
## it ate the clown?

| because | growl | but | huge |
|---|---|---|---|
| his | brought | did | long |
| not | he | she | was |
| back | great | tasted | breath |
| funny | wrong | strange | again |

1. Get rid of words with three letters.

2. Cross out words containing G.

3. Lose any words that start with B.

What do clowns wear to go swimming?
Giggles!

# TO THE RESCUE!

Omegaman and his sidekick Delta have swung into this party to save the day! How many hidden party horns can you find?

**How do the Malfoys enter a party?**
They Slytherin!

# PERFECT PET

If you were allowed any pet in the world, what would you choose? Draw it here!

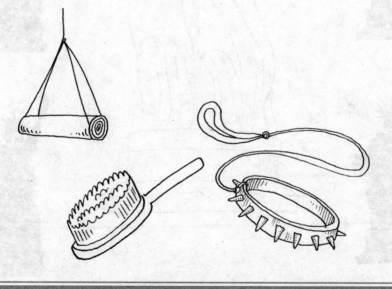

**Why did the soldier put a tank in his house?**
It was a fish tank!

# LADY LIBERTY

Welcome to the USA! Study the famous Statue of Liberty and then see which of the silhouettes is an exact match.

**Why does the Statue of Liberty stand in New York?**
Because it can't sit down!

# THE SILVER SADDLE

Welcome to the Silver Saddle Saloon! See if you can find the smaller squares somewhere in the main picture. Write the grid reference for each one.

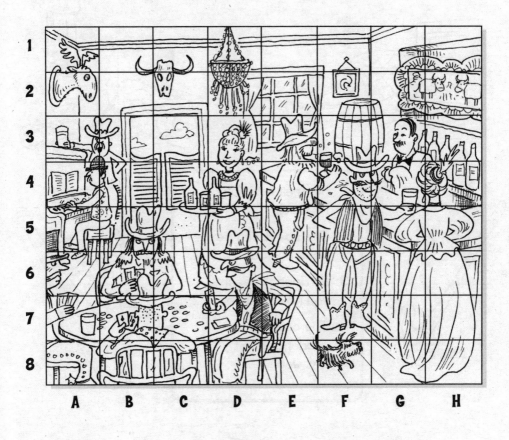

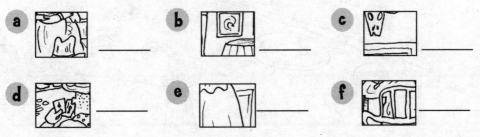

**Why did the restaurant on the Moon have to close?**
There was no atmosphere!

193

# COACH GOODWAY

What sport does Coach Goodway teach?
Use the clues to work it out.

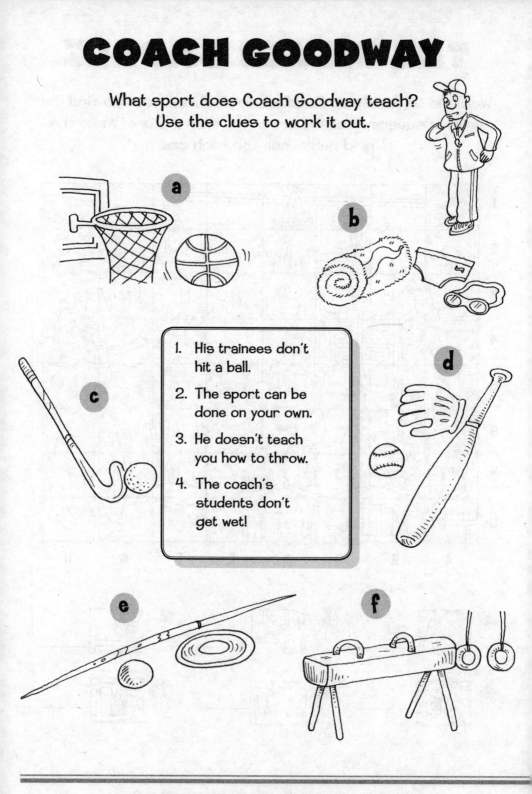

a

b

1. His trainees don't hit a ball.

2. The sport can be done on your own.

3. He doesn't teach you how to throw.

4. The coach's students don't get wet!

c

d

e

f

Why would you take a baseball glove on a surfing trip?
So you could catch a wave!

# TALL AND SMALL

Look carefully at the mixed up picture. Draw each of the squares in the correct place on the grid to put the picture back together again.

**What did the tree do when the library was closed?**

It tried another branch!

# HELP ME!

Captain Schnurrbart to the rescue!
Look carefully to find six differences
between these two scenes.

**Which capital city is growing at the fastest rate?**
Dublin!

196

# BIRD TALK

Cross out every other letter, starting with "T" and moving clockwise, to find out where this chatty pet would live in the wild.

A T A S
L / S
i U
E M
L S
Z N
A W R E T

What birds are commonly found in Portugal?

Portu-geese!

# SNORKEL SCARE

Put these pictures in the correct order to tell the story properly.

**Where do mermaids watch movies?**
At the dive-in!

# ON THE LOOKOUT

There's a new bad guy in town! Finish this Wild West wanted poster with your own cowboy criminal.

**Why did Al Capone fire his cleaner?**
He wanted to be a famous grime lord!

# WIN OR LOSE?

Shade in all the squares containing F, L, and O. The remaining letters will spell the answer to the joke below.

| L | O | F | O | O | L | B | O | E | L |
|---|---|---|---|---|---|---|---|---|---|
| O | C | O | A | F | U | L | O | F | O |
| L | O | O | L | F | L | F | S | E | F |
| F | H | O | L | O | F | O | O | L | F |
| F | L | E | F | O | L | O | L | O | L |
| O | F | L | O | K | F | L | F | L | O |
| E | F | O | F | L | L | P | F | O | T |
| F | D | O | L | L | R | L | F | A | L |
| O | L | W | I | L | F | O | L | O |   |
| L | O | F | F | O | L | N | G | O | F |

## Why didn't the artist ever win at sports?

_____ __ ____ _____!

---

**Why did cave people paint pictures of hippopotamuses?**
They couldn't spell it!

# ICE, ICE BABY

Solve the sums and find a path across the ice, stepping only on answers that are odd numbers.

$6 \times 8$

$53 - 21$

$45 \div 5$

$7 \times 3$

$24 + 54$

$66 - 34$

$16 + 19$

$56 - 8$

$38 + 38$

$64 \div 8$

$96 - 27$

$7 \times 6$

$4 \times 12$

$11 \times 3$

**Can you name five animals found at the North Pole?**
"Four seals and a polar bear?"

201

# SUPERFOODS

Use the grid references to write down the correct letters.
They will spell out Captain Cobalt's top choice on a menu.

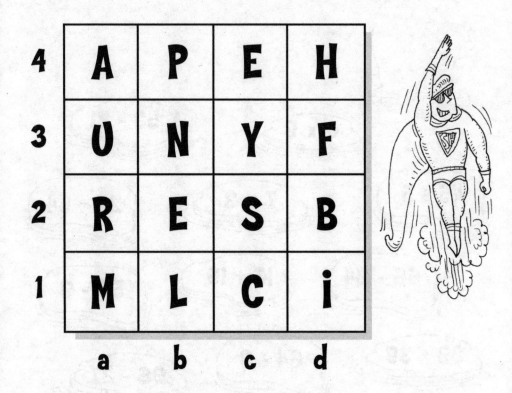

| | a | b | c | d |
|---|---|---|---|---|
| **4** | A | P | E | H |
| **3** | U | N | Y | F |
| **2** | R | E | S | B |
| **1** | M | L | C | i |

d2 b1 a3 b2 d2 c4 a2 a2 c3   b4 d1 c4

___ ___ ___ ___ ___ ___ ___ ___ ___   ___ ___ ___

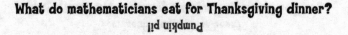

---

**What do mathematicians eat for Thanksgiving dinner?**
Pumpkin pi!

# IT'S A STICK UP

## How many stick insects are hiding here?

**Which knight hid around corners to make people jump?**
Sir Prise!

# MAKING CAMP

Use the clues to work out what each of the girls is camping in, and where they are going.

|  | Tent | Camper van | Tepee |
|---|---|---|---|
| **Amy** |  |  |  |
| **Leigh** |  |  |  |
| **Millie** |  |  |  |

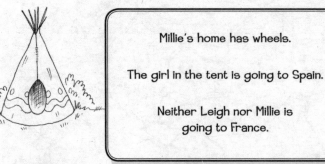

Millie's home has wheels.

The girl in the tent is going to Spain.

Neither Leigh nor Millie is going to France.

|  | France | Italy | Spain |
|---|---|---|---|
| **Amy** |  |  |  |
| **Leigh** |  |  |  |
| **Millie** |  |  |  |

---

**Why didn't the pixie invite his school friend for supper?**

His mother couldn't stand the goblin!

# OUTLAWED

Billy the Kid has escaped from jail! Follow the directions to find out where he's hiding.

1. After leaving jail, in C3, he headed 1 square south for the border, but went 2 squares east to avoid the huts.

2. At the mountains he cut south again for 1 square, crossed the border, and ran 3 squares west.

3. He sneaked 4 squares north, past Lone Pine Ridge and the church.

4. At the Rio Grande river he headed east 1 square, then north 1 square, then east 1 square again. Where should the sheriff look for him?

**Who was the most feared gunfighter in the ocean?**
Billy the Squid!

# THE WINNER IS...

You decide! Draw the race winners on the podium.
They can be competitors in any sport you like.

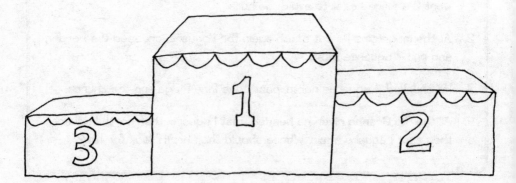

**What cat will never make a good pet?**
A cat-astrophe!

# ANIMAL MUDDLE!

What on earth is a ferkey? Or a waltle? Hang on a minute, these animal names are all mixed up! Split them up and put them back together properly to spell six real animals.

FER | KEY

MON | SEL

_____  _____

WAL | TLE

TUR | VER

_____  _____

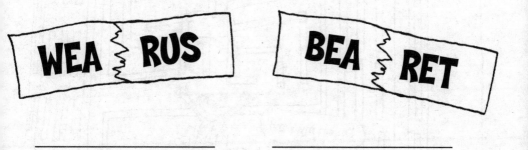

WEA | RUS

BEA | RET

_____  _____

**Why did the turkey want to join a band?**
Because he already had the drumsticks!

# STRANDED

Daisy Dolittle is stranded on top of the maze tower in Dubai! Only Spiderguy can help! Find a way up the building to rescue Daisy, and then back down the other side.

**Why did Little Miss Muffet need a map?**
Because she'd lost her whey!

# PUT IN THEIR PLACE

Put the pets in the sudoku grid so that each row, column, and mini-grid has only one of each type.

**What kind of pizza do dogs order?**
Pupperoni!

# CITY SEARCH

Where is Vicky going for her special trip? Look along each row to find one letter that appears in every city name. Find all six letters to spell her vacation destination.

| | | | |
|---|---|---|---|
| VERSAILLES | AVIGNON | VIENNA | VILNIUS |
| SAN DIEGO | SEVILLE | ZAGREB | ROME |
| MILAN | MONTREAL | DUBLIN | SYDNEY |
| LIMA | SOFIA | PARIS | KINGSTON |
| CARDIFF | VALENCIA | CALAIS | MOSCOW |
| NEW YORK | CANBERRA | PRAGUE | SEOUL |

___

___

___

___

___

___

**What is the fastest country in the world?**
Rush-a!

# CATCHING CATTLE

These cattle have been branded to show who owns them.
Match each one to its owner by solving the questions.

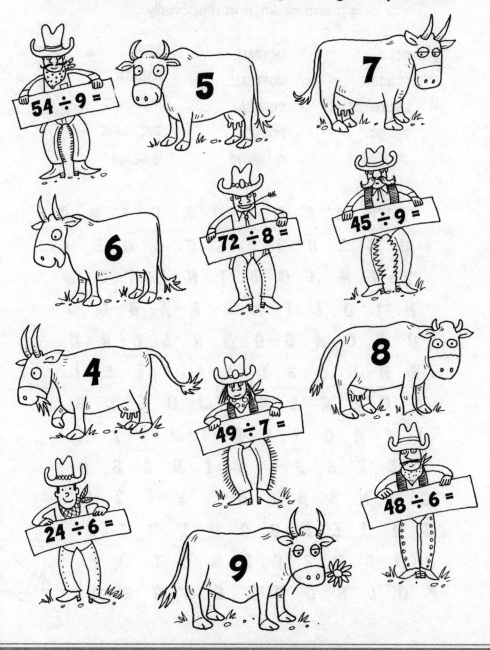

$54 \div 9 =$

5

7

6

$72 \div 8 =$

$45 \div 9 =$

4

$49 \div 7 =$

8

$24 \div 6 =$

9

$48 \div 6 =$

**How did Jack count how many beans his cow was worth?**
He used a cow-culator!

# SPORTS SEARCH

Look carefully in the grid to find 15 sports that don't hit the headlines all the time. They can be hidden across, up and down, and diagonally.

POLO     NETBALL     JUDO

FENCING     SOFTBALL     KARATE

LACROSSE     SURFING     SNOOKER

DIVING     BOULES     DRESSAGE

SQUASH     CLIMBING     HURLING

| S | K | A | R | N | S | U | R | F | i | N | G |
|---|---|---|---|---|---|---|---|---|---|---|---|
| U | G | S | D | R | E | S | S | A | G | E | i |
| R | N | N | J | U | D | T | N | E | T | S | N |
| H | i | O | L | P | N | S | B | A | B | U | G |
| U | C | O | A | S | O | Q | R | A | C | R | N |
| R | N | K | C | S | O | A | A | J | L | L | i |
| L | E | E | R | E | K | S | J | U | L | L | B |
| i | F | R | O | R | E | H | V | D | i | A | M |
| N | E | T | S | D | i | V | i | N | G | B | i |
| G | J | H | S | A | U | Q | S | V | i | T | L |
| S | Q | U | E | P | B | O | U | L | D | F | C |
| J | U | D | D | R | E | S | S | O | L | O | P |
| P | O | L | B | O | U | L | E | S | Q | S | Q |

---

**Alan: Is my dinner ready? I have karate class in an hour.**

Mother: Your chops are on the table!

# CREATURE COUNT

Study this picture of the rain forest canopy and see how many of each creature you can count.

Butterflies = [ ]     Snakes = [ ]

Beetles = [ ]     Birds = [ ]

**What kind of snake is good at mathematics?**
An adder!

# FALLING OR FLYING?

Super-Pete is holding on to something, but is he flying or hitching a lift? You decide, and draw what's high in the sky with him.

**What do you do if your pet mouse falls in the bath?**
Give it mouse-to-mouse resuscitation!

# GO, GINNY, GO!

Help Ginny the guinea pig find her way to her friends by following the arrows in the right direction each time.

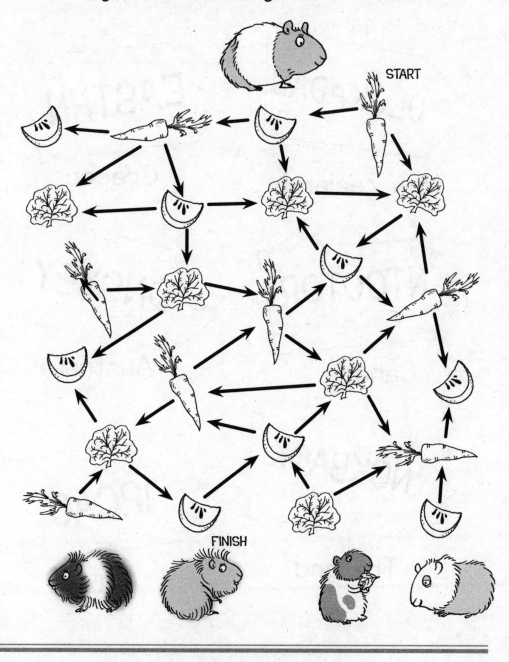

START

FINISH

**What did the Easter bunny say to the carrot?**
"It's been nice gnawing you!"

215

# OFF WE GO!

Unscramble the letters on each luggage label to find out which cities everyone is going to on their travels.

ULCKADAN

New Zealand

EASTHN

Greece

NTOOTOR

Canada

DNSYEY

Australia

NGKBAOK

Thailand

IRCAO

Egypt

**Did you hear about the Greek god who spilled juice on the carpet?**

He Apollo-gized again and again!

# BIRD'S EYE VIEW

Study the shootout picture, and then decide which of the smaller pictures is the correct bird's eye view of the scene.

**What do you call a frog who wants to be a cowboy?**
Hopalong Cassidy!

# SPORTS CAMP

Find out what the two most popular camp activities are by writing down the pairs of letters for each grid reference.

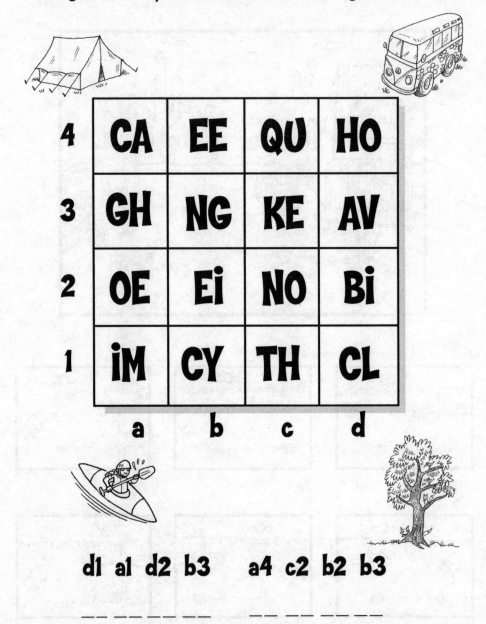

| | a | b | c | d |
|---|---|---|---|---|
| 4 | CA | EE | QU | HO |
| 3 | GH | NG | KE | AV |
| 2 | OE | Ei | NO | Bi |
| 1 | iM | CY | TH | CL |

**d1 a1 d2 b3    a4 c2 b2 b3**

__ __ __ __    __ __ __ __

**Why shouldn't you build a fire in a kayak?**

You can't have your kayak and heat it!

# FOOTPRINTS

The mini-grid appears only once in the whole of the larger grid. Can you find it?

**What do you say when it rains ducks and chickens?**
"Fowl weather, isn't it?"

219

# LASER LINES

Fill in the blanks using the letters RAYGUN, in any order, so that every row, column, and mini-grid contains each letter only once.

**Which emperor should have stayed away from gunpowder?**
Napoleon Blownaparte!

220

# STABLE SHADOWS

Look carefully at the picture of Belinda with her pony.
Which of the silhouettes matches it exactly?

What do you call a wizard on a horse?
Harry Trotter!

# CITYSCAPE

Finish the buildings and add your own designs
to make a city you would love to explore.

**Why did the bridge get angry?**
Because people were always crossing it!

# YEEHAW!

## Which two of these cowboys are exactly the same?

**Why didn't anyone laugh at the farmer's jokes?**
They were too corny!

223

# MUSCLE MAN

Use the grid references to write down the correct letters. They will spell out what sport this muscle man competes in.

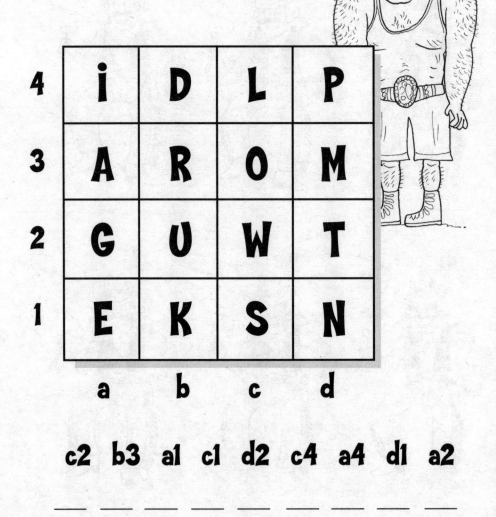

| | a | b | c | d |
|---|---|---|---|---|
| 4 | i | D | L | P |
| 3 | A | R | O | M |
| 2 | G | U | W | T |
| 1 | E | K | S | N |

c2  b3  a1  c1  d2  c4  a4  d1  a2

___  ___  ___  ___  ___  ___  ___  ___  ___

---

**What did one beach say to the other beach?**

"Show me your mussels!"

# A PRICKLY SITUATION

Can you find a way through this porcupine's prickly quill maze?

START

FINISH

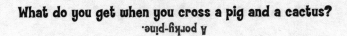

**What do you get when you cross a pig and a cactus?**
A porky-pine.

# A BUSY DAY

Help Captain Flash rescue everyone! You must use the paths to pass through each circle, using only one straight line to connect each one. You aren't allowed to travel along the same path twice.

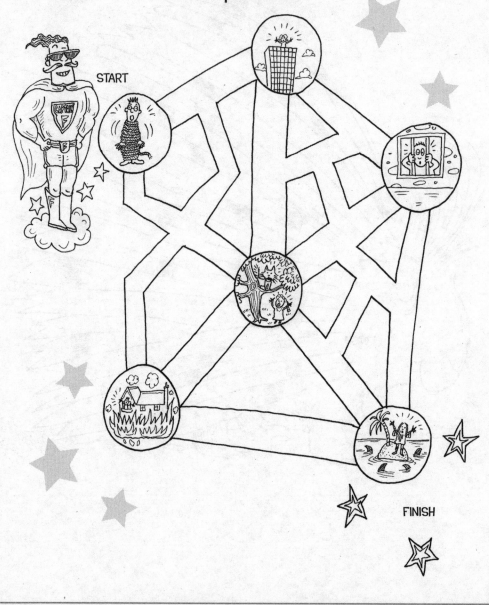

# NIGHT VISION

What kind of animal is peering at you from this page?
Finish the picture, making it cute, fierce, or totally freaky!

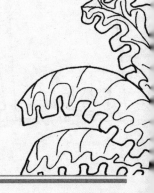

**Why do dragons sleep all day?**
So they can fight knights!

# ON THE PROWL

Look carefully at the mixed up picture. Draw each of the squares in the correct place on the grid to put the picture back together again.

**Did you hear about the cat that swallowed a ball of yarn?**
She had mittens!

228

# TRAIL FINDER

Draw who has made these footprints... and what is following close behind!

**How can you tell that an elephant has been in your fridge?**
From the footprints in the butter!

**229**

# TROPICAL TANK

This fish tank needs something in it. Can you draw some fabulous fish, and add some furniture for them to swim around?

**Where can you take a pet cat for a day trip?**
To the mew-seum!

# ANSWERS

## 3  LOOKING LOST

## 4  HOLIDAY READING

BUSH CRAFT

## 6  BIRD BRAINS

## 7  RAFT RACE

**8    BY THUNDER!**
JUPITER

**9    SNOW SHOES**
b

**11   FEARSOME FUNGUS**
DESTROYING ANGEL

**12   TINY TERRORS**

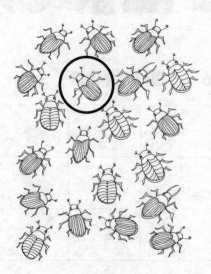

**13   DUCK BILLS**
8 x 12 = 3 x 32
(both = 96)

**15   BLIZZARD WARNING**
18

**16   MAP IT OUT**

**17   HOWL DO YOU DO?**
Here are some you
may have found:
fourth, energy, fire,
golf, thrill, north,
tower, thief, light,
huge.

**18   SEVEN SALMON SWIMMING**

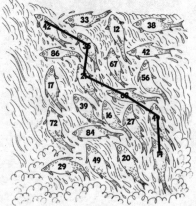

## 19 LET US PRAY

e

## 20 BIRD LOVERS

Tim is with his grand-
dad and sees the
ostrich.
Lucy sees the stork
with her dad.
Alex and his aunt go
to see the vulture.

## 21 TREASURE MAP

ANGLERFISH

## 23 JUNGLE EXPLORERS

```
G J E G U G J G U J
J L J J J E N U N U
U G L E C J G U N G
N G E L G N U J U U
L J E C U E J U G J
G U L N G U G J E N
U U J U E L G U J J
G G U J G J G L E L
J U G U J G J J G E
J J U N C L E J U G
```

## 24 TIGER FEET

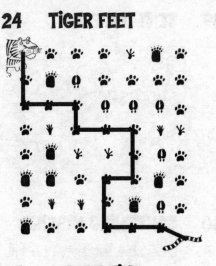

## 25 A RARE FIND

## 26 ON THE WING

LUNA MOTH

## 28 FISHING FRENZY

The girl has earned
more points: 58
(the boy has 56).

## 29 TENT-ING FATE!

## 30 SOMETHING MISSING

Use the letter A to fill the gaps:
ATACAMA
PATAGONIAN
SAHARA
ARABIAN
KALAHARI
CHIHUAHUAN

## 31 LAZY BONES

½ of 28 gives the biggest number (14).

## 32 SNAKES ALIVE!

4

## 33 READY, AIM, FIRE!

BOMBARDIER BEETLE

## 34 BIRDS OF A FEATHER

## 35 STAR PUPIL

21

## 37 COMPASS POINTS

11 compasses; 7 are not pointing north

## 38 ZOO-DOKU

Beccy wants to see number 4, the giraffe.

## 39  A WONDERFUL WORLD

You may have found: cello, office, rice, eel, fierce, reef, coffee, ice, for, roll.

## 40  ON THE ROCKS

Jon found a starfish.

## 41  WEATHER FORECAST

Delete the letter T from the first (lefthand) line. Delete A from the second line, P from the third line, W from the fourth line, and K from the last line. This gives the saying:
A WIND FROM THE SOUTH HAS RAIN IN ITS MOUTH.

## 43  BLACK AND WHITE

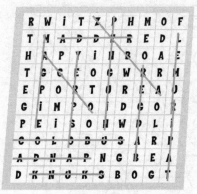

## 44  GOING NUTTY

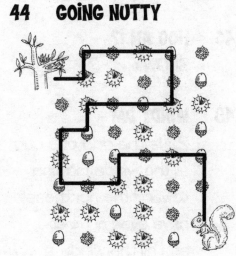

## 45 BEETLE RUN

## 46 HOO AM i?
SNOWY

## 48 WiNDY DAY
22 is the odd one out;
all the winds blowing
toward the northeast
have even numbers
and all the winds
blowing toward
the east have odd
numbers, except for
that one.

## 49 MiGHTY MAYA

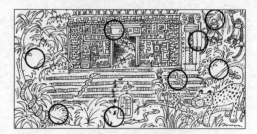

## 50 WiLD THiNGS
Hyena, alligator,
baboon, jaguar, gorilla,
coyote

## 49 MEGA BLAST
$60 \div 20 + 50 - 3 \times 2 = 100$

## 53 NO PLACE LiKE HOME
RAZORBILL
KING PENGUIN
CUCKOO
EAGLE OWL

## 54  SUPERSTARS

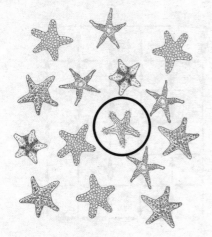

## 55  TWISTER
b

## 57  WONDER-FALL

## 58  LEAF IT OUT

## 59  A BUG'S LIFE
Here are some you may have found: bump, point, get, open, menu, bonus, begin, tongue, toes, pigeon.

## 60  WALK THE WALK

## 61 SIREN SONG
d

## 62 BIRTHDAY BONANZA
Bill is going bowling on Tuesday. Jill is going to the movies on Monday. Will will go skating on Wednesday.

## 63 LET'S EXPLORE
Captain James T. Kirk is a character from the film Star Trek. He's not real!

## 65 FLOWER POWER

## 66 SNAIL TRAIL

## 67 EGGS-STRAORDINARY

## 68 DEEP THOUGHTS
MARIANA TRENCH
It is in the Pacific Ocean which, in code, is this:
a4.d1.d2.d3.c1.d3.d2

**70 SNOW PROBLEM!**
37 (starting at 1 and moving clockwise, add 1, then add 2, then add 3 and so on)

**71 IN THE WILD**

**72 FALLING TREASURE**
a. ACORN
b. CHESTNUT
c. BEECHNUT
d. PINE CONE

**73 HIGH JUMP**
a

**74 LEGGY LOVELIES**
19

**75 SEA MONSTER**
GIANT GROUPER

**76 CRYSTAL CLEAR**

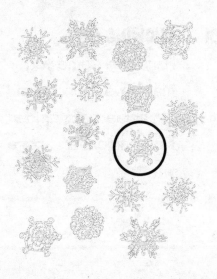

**87 NICE NEST**

The word WASP
appears 5 times.

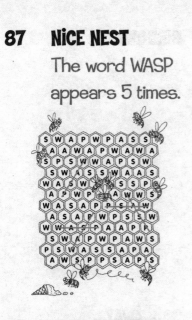

**88 EGG-CELLENT**

**89 COMING UP**

**90 HURRICANE HUNT**

HURRICANE GEORGE

**92 ANIMAL ADDITION**

**93 WILD AND WONDERFUL**

**94 FEELING HUNGRY**

LATERAPPCIL

**95 BIG BIRD**

d

## 96 ON THE ROCKS

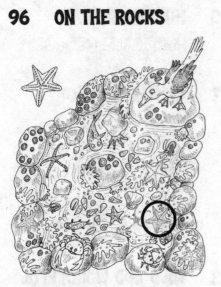

## 97 HIGH AND DRY
ATACAMA DESERT

## 98 TWO TRIBES
f

## 99 BIG BABY
c (both = 75)

## 101 CREATURES COUNT
15

## 102 BIRDOKU

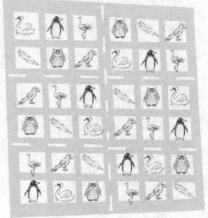

## 103 SAIL AWAY
Here are some you may have found: eagle, ant, genie, giant, alien, visit, slight, steal, sigh, last.

## 104 ON STRIKE

## 105 YEAR OF THE DRAGON
f

## 106 FEEDING TIME
The tapir is fed at 10am and Amelie goes to watch. The zebra feed is at 1pm and Jenny watches. Mark watches the panda feed at 3pm.

## 107 POND DIPPING
TADPOLE

## 109 A RARE BIRD

K P K K A P A K A K
P A O A O A K A P A
O K K A K P O A K O
K A A A K P O A A P
A K K P A O K K A A
P K A K K A P O K K
K A A O P O K A O O
A O P A K A K A P K
O P O A K A K K A P
A K A K P A K A K O

## 110 SHE SELLS SEASHELLS

## 111 UNDER THE WEATHER

**112 UNITED STATES**
ARKANSAS
OKLAHOMA
KENTUCKY
VIRGINIA
DELAWARE
COLORADO
NEBRASKA
MICHIGAN
ILLINOIS
MISSOURI

**114 SEASONAL SUMS**
a. 20
b. 22
c. 19
d. 21

**115 BUSY BEES**

**116 LOVE BIRDS**
CANARY
FINCH
PARROT
PIGEON
VULTURE
MACAW

**117 UNDER THE SEA**
1272

**118 TORNADO TROUBLE**
12

**119 AROUND THE WORLD**
AGE OF DISCOVERY

**120 SPOTTED!**

## 121 SQUIRREL SQUARE

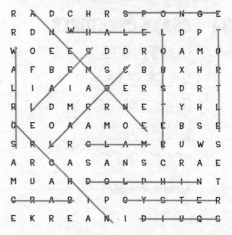

= x    = ÷

= +    = −

## 123 BUSY BIRDS

There are 16 nests and 15 birds.

## 124 THREE IN A ROW

## 125 A SUNNY OUTLOOK

Here are some you may have found: moon, rush, sir, sign, hung, grin, monsoon, ring, union, rhino.

## 126 THE GREAT DIVIDE

The only number left is 22.

## 127 MEET THE MEERKATS

e

## 128 NATURE LOVER

Stacey buys the fox t-shirt.

## 129 BUGGING OUT

GLOWWORM
COCKROACH
DRAGONFLY
CENTIPEDE
MOSQUITO

## 131 CLUELESS CREATURES

```
R A D C H R S P O N G E
R D N W H A L E L D P T
W O E E S D D R O A M U
A F B E M S C B B X H P
L I A I A G E R S D R T
R L D M R R N E T Y H L
U E O A A M O E C B S E
S R L R C L A M R U W S
A R C A S A N S C R A E
M U A H D O L P H I N T
C R A B I P O Y S T E R
E K R E A N I D I U Q S
```

## 132 FOLLOW MY LEMUR

## 133 WHITEOUT!

## 134 CRAZY CREATURES

CHIMPANZEE,
WILDEBEEST,
RHINOCEROS,
SALAMANDER,
KOOKABURRA,
CHINCHILLA

## 136 BEING BUGGED

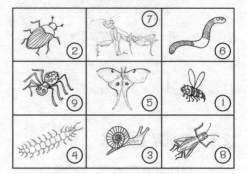

## 137 ALL TOGETHER NOW

## 138 A – B – SEA

✳ = B

★ = A

☆ = C

## 139 LIGHTNING STRIKES

a

## 140 DESERTED

c

**141  WILD THING**
It is called a platypus. It has venomous stingers on its feet. It is a mammal but lays eggs. Only the babies have teeth.

**142  FLUTTERBY**
d

**143  A REAL STINGER**
Add the first two numbers in each row, then add 2, to give the next number. So the missing numbers are: 43, 7, 16, 6.

**145  SURF'S UP**

**146  WHATEVER THE WEATHER**

**147  SIGHTSEEING**
Here are some you may have found: hero, flower, front, dense, feeds, sewed, herself.

**148  WANDERING WOMBATS**
c

**149  BLAST ZONE**
d

**150  WHO GOES THERE?**
Amy finds a beetle in a tree. Ben finds a centipede on a rock. Charlie finds a moth in the hedge.

## 151  THINK PINK
SHRIMP

## 153  STICK WITH IT
30

## 154  SUPER SHOOTERS
Strength

## 155  JUST JOKING
Because they have
nine lives!

## 156  CIAO ITALIA!
Pisa, Rome, Milan,
Naples

## 157  POWWOW, NOW!
c

## 159  EAGLE EYES
a. D2
b. H8
c. G1
d. E6
e. A5
f. B2

## 160  BETTER, FASTER, HIGHER
a = 152
b = 151
c = 151

## 161  IT'S A MYSTERY

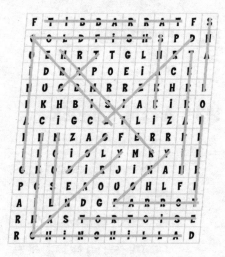

## 162  FUN IN THE SUN

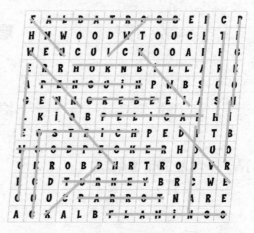
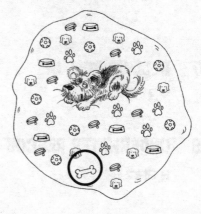

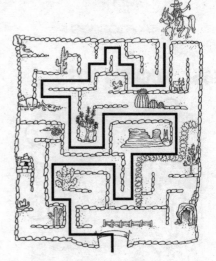

## 185 CUDDLY CREATURES
1. Peacock
2. A3
3. C4
4. E5
5. Piglets
6. Llamas

## 186 GET PACKING
The paired items are: flip flops, bucket (pail) and spade, face mask and snorkel, notepad and pen, toothbrush and toothpaste.

## 187 THE LONE RANGER

## 188 SPORTS SQUARE

## 189 LION LAUGHS
He tasted funny

## 190 TO THE RESCUE!
There are ten party horns.

## 192 LADY LIBERTY
e

## 193 THE SILVER SADDLE

a. D5
b. F2
c. C2
d. B7
e. H6
f. B8

## 194 COACH GOODWAY

f—he coaches
gymnastics

## 195 TALL AND SMALL

## 196 HELP ME!

## 197 BIRD TALK

Australia

## 198 SNORKEL SCARE

e, f, a, c, b, d

## 200 WIN OR LOSE?

Because he kept
drawing!

## 201 ICE, ICE BABY

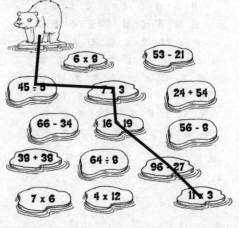

**202 SUPERFOODS**

Blueberry pie

**203 IT'S A STICK UP**

12

**204 MAKING CAMP**

Amy is going to
France in a tepee.
Leigh is going to
Spain in a tent.
Millie is going to Italy
in a camper van.

**205 OUTLAWED**

They should look
behind Wild Cat
Mountain (D6).

**206 ANIMAL MUDDLE!**

Ferret, monkey, walrus,
turtle, weasel, beaver

**208 STRANDED**

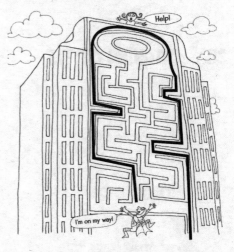

**209 PUT IN THEIR PLACE**

## 210 CITY SEARCH
Venice

## 211 CATCHING CATTLE
$24 \div 6 = 4$
$72 \div 8 = 9$
$48 \div 6 = 8$
$54 \div 9 = 6$
$45 \div 9 = 5$
$49 \div 7 = 7$

## 212 SPORTS SEARCH

## 213 CREATURE COUNT
Butterflies = 15
Beetles = 10
Snakes = 6
Birds = 8

## 215 GO, GINNY, GO!

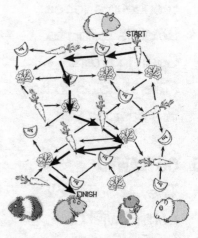

## 216 OFF WE GO!
Auckland, New Zealand
Athens, Greece
Toronto, Canada
Sydney, Australia
Bangkok, Thailand
Cairo, Egypt

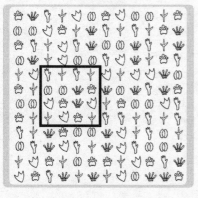

## 226  A BUSY DAY

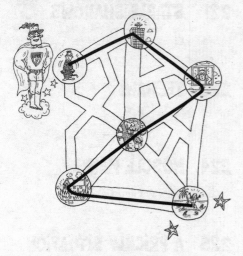

## 228  ON THE PROWL